The Traveler's Secret

Ancient Proverbs For Better Living

MICHAEL V. IVANOV

For fifteen very special humans,
>my wife MaKenzie Ivanov,
>Dad and Mom Ivanov,
>Olga Ivanov,
>Elijah Ivanov,
>Andrey Ivanov,
>Julie Ivanov,
>Igor Ivanov,
>Paul Ivanov,
>Tim Ivanov,
>Dennis Ivanov,
>Erik Ivanov,
>Elizabeth Ivanov,
>Nellie Ivanov,
>Lia Ivanov,
>. . . and their ever-expanding families

Other books by Michael V. Ivanov

The Mount of Olives:
11 Declarations to an Extraordinary Life

The Servant With One Talent:
Five Success Principles from the Greatest Parable
Ever Told

The Cabin at the End of the Train:
A story about pursuing dreams

Contents

Chapter 1
The Watering Hole

Long, long ago, on a winter night colder and darker than a night had been before, a lowly figure trudged through a freshly laid blanket of snow.

The sound of footsteps sinking into the white powder and the endless whistle of wind echoed in the eerie night as the silhouette pushed forward. Nearly the entire village in the northern region of Gallia Celtica, or Gaul, as it is now remembered, was already asleep, but a faint chorus of liquored-up voices singing to the whine of a fiddle floated through the winds.

"A drink . . . I can get a drink," the miserable vagabond mumbled. His feet moved more rapidly.

Just an hour before, he had been rudely awakened by the clamor of barn doors being thrown open by a torch-wielding farmer. The barn had provided shelter from the bitter cold until the sheep, who heated the hay he slept on, had become restless.

Perhaps they could no longer bear the smell of the human who had joined them for the evening, or perhaps they feared him, but something caused the animals to lose trust in their visitor and begin bleating nervously and loudly. He treasured the warmth of the fat complainers but now cursed them for giving him away.

Just before the farmer's torch illuminated him in his hiding place, he sprinted for the door and out into the cold. He ran and did not stop until the wind had swallowed the angry shouts behind him.

With a torn blanket wrapped around his shoulders, he leaned into the blizzard and followed a road that led past farm fields and forests. Only the fence posts marked the plots which in the summertime burst with wheat or corn. In the winter, and on this night, the snow-covered fields only reminded him of his own little world: barren and dead. He was cold, his stomach was empty, and he was alone.

The blowing snow hypnotized him nearly to sleep, but the burn of his frozen, tired feet kept him moving. He pulled the blanket tighter across his chest and pressed on.

The dark figure moved along the road, which curved around a frozen hilltop and brought him into a sleepy village. He walked past stone huts with straw-covered roofs that barely supported the weight of the snow, following the slurred voices until he finally reached his destination. A snow-covered sign hung just above the door with letters crudely carved into the wood: "The Watering Hole." He shouldered open the door of dried reeds and brushed past the cowhide hung to hold the winds from blowing into the tavern.

The warmth of the center fire hugged his body, and he stood for a moment in the doorway to thaw.

As the fiddle played and the drunken men howled in unison a few notes behind, the vagabond scanned the room, with its low beams of seasoned timber, and spotted a table closer to the double-sided stone fireplace. Heat pulsated from the smooth river stones of the chimney; the fire place opening darkened by endless fires was a priceless luxury in the winter months.

Torches were fastened to the thick log posts holding the crossbeams and burned at eye-level. Their flames illuminated the dark corners of the tavern where the slightly more sober patrons sat at a distance from the ruckus, engaged in conversations drowned out by the singing.

He inhaled the smell of fermented beer spilled on the tables as he passed, longing for a taste of the magic potion which always seemed to make his problems more bearable. But there were no coins in his pockets. There hadn't been for a long time.

At least I can blend in with this bunch and warm up, he thought. Some of the men leaned on one another, snoring. Others had their heads down on the tables. Not a soul cared to notice him, and that was the way he liked it. Until the tavern closed, he could enjoy the warmth and let his damp clothes dry a little.

He slowly bent down to loosen the frozen leather strings on his brogans. He'd wrapped rabbit fur tight around his calves and pulled the wet hide apart to rub the soggy trousers sticking to his legs. He took the blanket from his shoulders, laid it across his knees, and inched himself closer to the flames, stretching a trembling hand to the heat. Barely thirty, he moved and shook like an old man.

The vagabond sat and shivered, staring at the fire, chin in his palms and elbows on his knees. Without a bellyful of beer to distract him, the thoughts he'd been avoiding settled in again as they always did.

"If they saw me like this, they couldn't bear it," he muttered under his breath.

He turned his eyes back to the doorway and imagined his mother and father stepping through it and seeing him so pitiful. Their only son, once filled with dreams and possibilities, now wasting away, stinking of sheep dung, hugging himself for warmth. Just another vagabond destined to a life of begging and scavenging.

He hadn't bathed in weeks and could not remember his last solid meal. The legumes he shared with the sheep just hours ago felt like sand in his belly.

In the flickering firelight, tears glistened on his frostbitten face. He closed his eyes and the memories came.

Chapter 2
The Days of Dreaming

One day, when he was nine years old, Agisillus was helping his mother and father in the fields when he heard the thunder of hooves. He ran and reached the edge of the field just in time to see a caravan led by an army of horsemen riding through the little village. He had never seen anything so grand.

The soldiers' polished shields gleamed in the sun, and the purple silk draped around the carriage billowed in the wind. Curiosity piqued, he ran alongside the carriage, barefoot. He caught a glimpse of a boy inside, not much older than himself, gazing out of the window. Their eyes met for a moment.

He stopped running after the carriage and looked back over his shoulder to see his mother and father in the field bent over their hoes, pulling clumps of dirt and rocks from the soil. Even from a distance, he could see his father's leathery, sunburned skin. He could see his mother's bare feet in the dirt and the veins on her legs that only seemed to show more every day. Just a week earlier, one of the veins had broken and he'd crouched in terror in the shadows of the hut as his father wrapped her legs to stop the bleeding.

He thought she was going to die.

There was always so much work to do that he rarely got to play with the other boys in the village. When he begged for permission to go swim at the lake, he was always reminded, "Winter is coming, and it will be a cold one this year."

It was the same every year. The coming winter was always going to be "the cold one." To the boy, once the snow came, it made no difference if it was knee-high one year and waist-high the next. The winters were equally miserable.

It's all anyone talked about in the village: "Work hard in summer so that you don't starve when the snow comes." They had done so every summer since he could remember. But he was already nine, and no matter how hard he worked, it was never enough to lighten his father's load. Oftentimes, he felt like he slowed their progress more than he helped. The metal hoe was heavy, and he had to tuck the handle under his armpit so he could lift it high enough to hack at the dirt. It was awkward and slow. His father would patiently follow behind him and till the same area all over again but never criticized him.

Agisillus stood in the road, the dirt underneath his fingernails drying in the breeze.

How was that boy in the carriage so lucky? He had pale skin and neatly trimmed hair. His fancy gold collar propped his chin high as he looked down from the giant carriage. He must have not had a care in the world, surrounded by an army of strong horseman, while Agisillus's own parents were wearing their bodies to old age, toiling under the sun. What about those other travelers who came through with large pouches of coins while so many villagers could not earn that amount in an entire lifetime of plowing fields, fishing, or hammering away in the blacksmith shops? If wealth came from hard work, shouldn't his mother and father be rich?

As he watched the caravan weave like a snake along the road until it disappeared around the mountain, Agisillus made a promise to himself. He would be rich one day, just like the boy in that caravan. His family would never work another day in the fields. He would wrap his mother's feet in the finest sandals, drape his father's shoulders with the thickest furs, and the three of them would finally be able to afford the sweet, aged wine at the tavern.

He remembered that day often—and cursed it each time. He remembered how his father had straightened up to see the caravan passing, wiping the sweat from his forehead. His father looked at Agisillus for a moment before a smile came across his face, spreading his thick mustache wide. He had just asked his father if they could be rich like the boy in the caravan.

"If God wills it, of course we can be rich!" his father said, breathing heavily. "Dreams are like fireflies . . . Do you see how they light up, signaling to attract a mate with their glow?"

Agisillus nodded as he scanned the fields. The fireflies always came out at dusk, and he loved watching them dance over the tall grass like sparks over a fire.

"They are searching for the perfect companion, and once they find one, together they create such beauty with their dance!" Father's voice grew quiet, as if he were telling a secret, and he crouched on one knee in the dirt until his face was close to Agisillus's, his eyes sparkling.

"Be like a firefly, boy. If your heart keeps glowing brightly, a dream will come to you, and your life, too, can be like a dance. You can be as rich as you would like!" He winked at the boy and then paused for a moment, holding onto the handle of the hoe, and stared into the hills.

"If only I could do it all again. If only I had one more try at this life, I wouldn't be so mindless and distracted. I wouldn't be so skeptical of the dreams I once had. I wouldn't be so full of fear. I made up excuses for why I could not take the opportunities that came my way, and did they come? Yes . . . too many to count. I won't get that time back." His tired green eyes squinted and grew dull as he left the distant memories and came back to look at the boy again.

"You see, your mother and I were born into a time of war, and we always had little. We hoped for much but believed very little was possible for us. I only wish we could have given you more, my boy, but if you wish to be more, listen carefully." His father paused for a long moment and looked away. Agisillus loved it when his father spoke to him like an adult. The man never hesitated to speak truthfully and honestly, even to a nine-year-old boy.

With his face still turned away, he finally spoke again.

"Dreams are the Creator's gift to us. They are his way of bringing us closer to his own heart. They are his dreams for us, and it is why he has given us the desire to seek them, a mind to order them, and a heart to make them come alive."

He paused again and glanced at the boy's mother before lowering his voice. "Every day, I am thankful to God for you and your mother. No matter if he makes us rich or leaves us poor, I will continue to thank him for the dance my life has already been, but I don't know how many more seasons your mother and I can toil this way. I see something extraordinary in you, boy. Don't work your life away like we did. Be wise, preserve your health. Look about you; look at how every man toils in this village. If you don't want to live like them, do not think like them. Do not think like we did for so long."

Agisillus wished he could forget the sorrow on his father's sun-beaten face. It was one of the clearest memories he had of the man, and he hated himself for having started the conversation that day. It was his naive questions that made his father relive his regrets.

The years came and went, and Agisillus watched his parents grow older and wished he could stop time. He wished he could think of a way to earn more money; he needed to. But the dream of being wealthy faded, as did his promise to himself.

It was difficult for him to dream like his father had taught him that day. It was difficult when all he could see was their deepening wrinkles and graying hair as the seasons passed.

He began to draw sketches of tools that might help his parents till the fields more efficiently and not take such a toll on their bodies. If they worked, perhaps he could even sell the tools to other farmers. But when he showed his sketches to other boys and explained his ideas, they laughed. "You fool—you think this pathetic drawing is going to make you wealthy and you'll rule over us all with your riches? You're a simpleton, just like your father. Don't forget that," they mocked.

In his village, the more muscle on the arms, fat on the belly, and hair on the chest one had, the more of a man one was. Agisillus had none of these attributes, but it did not matter to him. None of these would bring him closer to his dream.

The village men were like cattle: strong, tough, useful, but certainly not very clever. He wished they would understand him. With their blistered hands and constant complaining of 'bad luck,' wouldn't they be interested in discovering a better way to live? No one ever seemed to pick their head up high enough to see beyond the valley they'd inhabited for decades, and Agisillus began to feel excluded even among his friends.

A sweaty brow was proof of hard work, and he was no stranger to it working his father's fields, but he knew if one had enough wealth, one could simply employ other men who settled for the hard labor. He had been to large towns to the south when he traveled with his father to trade in the markets and noticed that not everyone needed to be a farmer to thrive.

In fact, he had heard the wealthy people barely worked and still got wealthier. They employed others to do the hard labor while they did the thinking. They didn't break their own backs in the fields; they let those who were satisfied with a few coins in exchange for labor do the hard work. Agisillus wanted to be a thinker, too, not a worker.

He quit speaking of his dreams, but for years the image of

a fat satchel of gold on his waist remained in his mind. He often stayed up late into the night, sketching ideas for new contraptions on his dried skins until it was time to head to the blacksmith shop. He'd started to work there instead of in the fields in hopes of earning more money.
He regularly heard the words of his father as clear as the day they were spoken, "If God wills it, of course we can be rich!" He never dared to tell his father for fear of disappointing the man; his father had been obsessed with the one God, "the Creator," as he often called him. But deep down, Agisillus concluded that even if there was a God, he wanted nothing to do with him. A God who blessed some people and starved others, even those who were faithful to him like his father was? Clearly God was a fraud.

One spring day as he was walking back from the shop, he scanned the fields as he always did, looking to see where his parents and neighbors were, how much they had tilled, and how much he'd be expected to do the next day. He spotted two figures lying on the partially tilled soil.
Agisillus ran as fast as he could until he reached them and dropped to his knees in the dirt. He shook his father's shoulders violently but the lifeless body was heavy. The man had curled into a ball like a sleeping baby, one hand still gripped the heavy iron hoe and the other clutched his chest. His mother's head lay gently on his father's side and her hands were wrapped around his forearms, as if she had been hanging on to him tightly in their final moments. Had their old and weary hearts finally failed trying to till the hard dirt?
Agisillus's body shook, but tears did not come as he sat in the dirt wrapping each of their lifeless and calloused hands into his own, kissing them over and over again.

That is how the villagers found him hours later just as the sun was setting.

After that day, he spoke very little and slept even less. His mind never stopped turning—over and over again seeing them in the field, replaying the caravan winding through town, remembering his promise to be rich so they wouldn't have to work. Hating himself for taking the job with the blacksmith. If only he had stayed where he belonged and wasn't so preoccupied with his ambitions, maybe they would still be alive.

Rumors had spread, and he heard most of them. Some said that he was too pampered and lazy as an only child and therefore was not there to help his parents. Some said his parents died in shame of him. Some even spread gossip that he did not care his parents were gone.

At times, he thought his head would split from the endless ruminating. In the tavern is where he found some relief. The barley beer became his medicine.

He began to stop by every day on his walk back from the blacksmith shop. One drink became two, and soon he wouldn't stop at three. Most nights he finally stumbled past the gate to his hut just before sunrise.

One evening, a woman had to carry him home when she found him on the road face down in the dirt. He woke the next day with urine on his trousers and vomit on his lips.

When the blacksmith finally let him go, citing his steadily decreasing production, he followed his routine and got drunk at the tavern with the money from his final payment. On his walk home he threw rocks and cursed loudly at every hut that he passed by, blaming the villagers for his misery.

"Sheep, the lot of you . . . sheep!" he screamed and

cupped his hand to make sheep noises at confused people in the street who stepped aside as he stumbled past. He gave so much weight to their words and opinions when he was sober, and he hated himself for it when he was drunk. It was the ongoing war between his two miserable worlds.

As he was fiddling with the latch on the gate, struggling to open it and barely standing, he turned to look at the road that led out of the village and twisted around the mountain, and he pictured the billowing purple fabric of the caravan from so many years ago.

He cursed the memory, cursed his dreams, cursed the village, cursed the people in it, cursed the sun and the moon, cursed the mountains and the valleys all around him, and he even cursed the heavens for being born.

He never made it past the gate in front of his hut. Instead, he turned and stumbled down the road.

Two years had gone since he wandered out of the village. That day Agisillus had sworn the townspeople would never see him again. As he crossed the bridge leaving the village, he flipped open his satchel and dumped his sketches in the creek. He watched them float away and then continued walking.

***

The fire cracked and Agisillus jerked. He quickly wiped his eyes and shook his head, looking around to see if anyone had noticed the tears. The men carried on singing and telling stories. He wondered what they were doing in the tavern so late. He had no other choice, but did they not have a bed or family to go home to?

Still chilled to the core, he could not keep his hands from shaking and hugged them around his belly, leaning closer to the flames.

The noise of the bar and the crackling of the fire didn't drown out the voice. The voice that reminded him he was far from the man he was supposed to be. The voice that reminded him of a time he wanted to be so much more. He wondered if each man in this tavern also heard a similar voice and was trying to silence it with ale and useless conversation. Perhaps they had also discovered that blaming others was the best way to excuse oneself from the burden of a dream.

He glanced at the half-full mug of beer on the table next to him. The man it belonged to was head-down, snoring. His long red mustache fluttered with every exhale, his eyes hidden by the braid drooping from his wolf-hide hat. Looking around, Agisillus reached out for the mug and slid it over to his chest. He waited for a moment and after he was certain the man was indeed fast asleep, he put the mug to his lips and drank. He felt the warmth of the alcohol spread to his belly. An empty stomach always got the job done faster, and these days it was empty most of the time.

Countless taverns had fallen victim to the vagabond's trick. He would sit at a table and drink until it was time to pay the tab. Then he would go outside to urinate, and instead of coming back in to settle his dues, he would walk off in a hurry. The only time he got caught was when he was in a large town, already occupied by the Romans.

That time the barkeep came outside, yelling down the street after him. Agisillus ran until his pants slipped off his thin waist and tangled around his feet, bringing him down hard to the ground. The passing Roman patrol witnessed the scene and grabbed Agisillus, laughing, as he drunkenly tried to stand. Weeks passed before the bruises and black eyes and humiliation finally faded away.

He glanced up at the barkeep busy tapping a fresh barrel. With his mean sneer, bald head, and broad shoulders, he looked like a man who could easily run Agisillus down if he skipped on a tab. He sipped his stolen beer more slowly. He didn't dare pull his signature move here.

Chapter 3
The Strange Traveler

The kick of the barkeep's foot against the bench startled him.

"Get going if you aren't buying," the large man's voice boomed in the dimly lit tavern. "This is no lodge."

Agisillus bent to tie the strings around his feet, cherishing the last moments near the fire. He pulled the strings tight and felt the damp hide close around his calves and immediately began to shiver again, fighting back tears. It was the second time this night he would have to head out into the cold.

He tugged the blanket tighter around his shoulders and

took one more longing look at the fire and its dancing flames before slowly hoisting his aching body off the bench.

If I kill myself, he thought, *there would be no more cold, no more starving, no more painful memories and humiliation, and no more god-damned walking in the snow. Besides, no one would miss a vagabond like me.* Impatient, the barkeep grabbed his collar and started toward the door.

***

"Oh, have a little mercy! How about a beer for the poor chap on me?" a loud voice rang from the doorway.

A giant man stood near the entrance, peeling off his fox-fur hat and letting long, matted hair drop to his shoulders. Icicles had formed on his untamed beard and a thin layer of snow coated the wide shoulders of his grizzled gray coat. He pulled the mittens from his massive hands, breathing into each cupped fist to warm them. Bushy brows further shadowed his deep-set eyes as he peered down at the vagabond.

The barkeep turned to look over his shoulder and then up at the man's face. When he became convinced the man was sincere, he dropped Agisillus's collar and headed for the bar.

Agisillus stole a cautious glance at the man and noticed the man staring back at him. He could feel the looks of several others around the room watching this encounter, perhaps to see if he'd be tossed out. He was not about to turn away an opportunity to stay in the warm tavern and slowly sat back down pretending to lose himself in the flames of the fire but could feel his face burning red, not so much warmed by the heat as humiliated by the unwanted attention.

He had the rest of the long night to follow through on his new plan and end his life, and he figured he could use this time to think it through. He tried not to look at the stranger as the barkeep filled two mugs.

The stranger grabbed the mugs and made his way toward the huddled vagabond, ducking his head under each beam. The generous mugs looked much smaller in his hands. He set them loudly on the tabletop, splashing drops of beer, and squeezed into the seat directly across from him. Agisillus hesitantly turned and pulled his feet over the split log bench to face the man.

The fire was at his back now, and he could see its glow reflecting in the man's dark eyes. His probing stare made Agisillus uncomfortable, and he shifted in the seat. The man looked at him intently, as if he knew him and was waiting to be recognized, but just as Agisillus opened his mouth to speak, the stranger broke the agonizing silence.

"You looked as if you could use a bit more time in here, and I wouldn't mind some company myself. Have the beer." He slid a mug toward Agisillus and took a sip from his own, leaving a thin line of foam at the bottom of his black mustache.

"Thank you," Agisillus managed to croak. The words came out hoarse, and he quickly cleared his throat. It had been days since he'd spoken audibly.

The stranger did not reply but studied the vagabond who cupped the mug with bony fingers and took a long gulp from his own. He kept his eyes on the young man, as if there was no one else in the tavern.

Agisillus set the mug down and exhaled heavily as if he had been holding his breath forever. As far as he was concerned, there weren't many things in the world more satisfying than beer, especially when he didn't have to steal it, and he instantly felt his body relax and the tension

18

release from his thin shoulders. He hoped it would divert the man's stare, and it seemed to.

The stranger's eyes appeared to smile, the wrinkles around them showing in the firelight, but his scraggily beard and mustache remained motionless after he wiped the foam from his lips. He reached up and combed his fingers through the long, mangled hair, pulling it back from his forehead and face.

"What do they call you?"

"Agisillus."

The man nodded knowingly but did not reveal his own name. His demeanor was intimidating to the vagabond who felt not a bone of confidence in his thin body.

He could hardly remember how it felt to be proud and to be noticed, to walk with head held high and shoulders back, to earn money after a day of hard labor and to be equal among men. Most days he tried to stay as small as possible with his head down and shoulders hunched, avoiding eye contact. There was not one village, town, or tavern he'd wandered through in which he hadn't walked by people apologetically, ducking out of the way to allow others to pass. Most days he hoped nobody would notice him.

The longer the stranger studied him, the lower Agisillus slouched in his seat. Surely the man didn't think much of him, but whatever he was thinking, it couldn't be worse than what he already believed about himself.

"Why are you here?" the stranger finally asked.

"It is warm in here," Agisillus replied, shrugging his shoulders. "I had nowhere else to go."

"A young man like you has nowhere to go, no woman to hold? No children to tuck in or fire to keep lit through the night?"

Now Agisillus realized he indeed would have to pay for his drink; he would pay with his time, trapped in a conversation he did not fancy being a part of. He wanted to be left alone and liked it better that way.

He was silent for a few moments and tried to come up with an excuse to get up and leave the conversation. Staying in the tavern across the table from this man meant he had beer and shelter from the blizzard but would have to answer these rude and prying questions.

"I have none of those things," he finally blurted out with a hint of frustration in his voice. "The Creator in his infinite wisdom has seen to that." His voice grew more assertive as he felt the built-up anger that was never very far from the surface.

He was proud of his response. It felt good to blame. He'd been carrying the shame for a long time—and he felt justified.

"I lost my mother and father because I wasted precious time chasing foolish daydreams instead of helping them on the farm. I once worked in a shop, thinking it would present a few more opportunities, but I managed to lose that too. Everything I ever touched turned to horse shit, and so here I am. No woman to hold, no children to tuck in, and no hut to keep warm through the night." His nose crinkled with disgust as he spilled his life struggle in a matter of seconds. If the man was going to ask intrusive questions, he'd gladly oblige him.

The stranger's eyebrows raised, and he stared at Agisillus, mug halfway to his mouth. His face turned from surprise to a slight smile. "Ahhhh, so the Creator hindered your dreams?"

Agisillus nodded hesitantly, realizing the question was sarcastic. He fiddled with the handle on the mug, suddenly feeling foolish. He had just swallowed the last of his beer and the man noticed the empty mug. His own was still nearly full. Agisillus played with the tarnished metal wrapping around the wooden mug and bone handle.

"And when did you arrive at this conclusion?" the man asked.

He didn't wait for an answer.

"A young man like you must be wise beyond your years to understand so much about the doings of the Creator and the pursuit of a dream. Share with me this knowledge. After all, I am old enough to be your father and there are dreams I am still hopeful for. Perhaps there was something I missed along the way—could it be that I am throwing my hopes to the wind?"

Agisillus felt his cheeks burning red. The stranger was finding humor in his story and he could feel anger welling up inside.

You might be old enough to be my father, but I'll bet you're half the man my father was. He could hardly keep the words to himself.

The way the man scanned his eyes from Agisillus to the mug, he likely had a good guess as to why the vagabond was in the position he was. Agisillus figured he was thinking it was alcohol that led him to ruin; it did for so many Gauls, but he didn't care. His circumstance was different.

"After I found my parents in that field, yes, I spent much time in the tavern. But it was the only way I could endure the days without going mad. I could not sleep, I could not work, and I could hardly eat. Some might say I am to blame, and perhaps I did give up altogether, but you will never know how hard I tried to succeed despite what happened—it was simply not meant to be."

Agisillus leaned toward the man and continued, "I was

going to see to it my parents never toiled again. It's all I wanted. But then everything crumbled, right before my eyes. If the Creator is not to blame, then who else is there?" He felt his voice crack and was surprised to find himself suddenly sharing so freely with the stranger.

The stranger had also leaned closer, no longer resting back on the bench. He seemed fascinated by the vagabond's story. These were questions Agisillus had chewed on again and again over the years, ruminating on them until he arrived at his conclusions.

"For many years I obsessed, thinking of ways to acquire money quickly. I watched my father and mother grow old each day, helpless. I thought, surely if the Creator gave me the inspiration for my dreams, then *he* would also show me how to attain them." He said, pointing toward the ceiling.

"I had ideas for farming tools but they were useless, because when I sketched and showed them to people, they scoffed."

The stranger listened with a half-smile as Agisillus retold his struggles.

"They called me 'lazy' because I wanted to create simpler ways to plow. I am not lazy; I've never shied away from hard work. But I could not keep my mind on work any longer, because I really thought I could do something extraordinary with my life. My father even saw that in me." The frustration in Agisillus's voice grew as the veins around his throat swelled.

The barkeep had occasionally glanced in their direction. His curiosity was piqued, and he quickly came over when the stranger waved his hand. The man grabbed Agisillus's empty mug and headed back to refill it.

"I'll get you another beer, and you may feel better for a while, but it won't do you much good to get drunk," the stranger said. "You can't get out of a problem in the same state of mind that got you into the problem. But you are free to choose of course."

"That's quite alright," Agisillus replied. "I'm not trying to solve my problems anymore. They are what they are; I've decided there is no use in fighting a power stronger than me. I'll let the Creator keep pouring on the troubles until he kills me altogether . . . or I'll do it myself."

The barkeep set the freshly filled mug on the table as he shouted at two drunken men who had begun to argue loudly. Agisillus had seen many fights break out from similar arguments and was relieved to see the barkeep squash the hostile disagreement quickly.

The old musicians played their tune as if nothing had happened. It was a typical evening for the three elderly men. They swayed in a synchronized motion, shirtsleeves rolled up to their forearms, masterfully handling their instruments. There was a fiddle and a lyre that looked to be a thousand years old, and a flute-like instrument Agisillus had not seen before. The group seemed to be thoroughly enjoying themselves as they drank between songs and talked amongst themselves.

The two sat in silence for a few minutes, and Agisillus sipped his beer, curious to know the stranger's name, but he decided he would ask when the man was ready to leave.

Finally, the man spoke: "It is amusing to me that you believed in a dream enough to try and pursue it, but when things became difficult—when the narrow thinking of others discouraged you—you quit. You wanted your life to be significant and to be respected by men who are doing no great things? *They* convinced you your ideas were worthless? And what weight did *their* opinions carry?

"Would a man who trusted God need the opinions of others in order to be confident about his dream?"

Agisillus shifted in his seat uncomfortably and turned to look behind him as if something had distracted him. Ever since he could remember, he had heavily relied on validation from others. And it *did* bother him when he couldn't get it, even though he pretended it didn't.

The stranger continued.

"I want to tell you something, but I'm not sure you're ready to hear it." He paused as if to decide whether he should ask the question but then continued. "In the hot desert far to the south of us, a mother wildebeest gives birth to a new calf. Can you guess why she would deny milk to her newborn baby?"

"Maybe she wants to teach him to stand up first? She doesn't want him to be lazy?" Agisillus guessed, but the stranger ignored him.

"People dream up things which the Creator would gladly fulfill, but they are so distracted, impatient, unbelieving, and easily discouraged, that when they are given the very thing they once asked for, they become like cowards simply because their dream comes disguised as a setback and is never easily achieved."

Agisillus dug his nails into the smoothly carved wood of the mug. He expected the man to have some grace after hearing his story, but the stranger seemed to find pleasure in using it against him. It was clear he was the calf in the story.

"Can you imagine how weak you would be if you had no struggles or obstacles? You would be like a daisy, dead at the first frost of fall. What kind of Creator would give you what you wanted just because you begged?

"A mother wildebeest does not feed its calf immediately upon birth. She knows they do not have much time. The lions are not far away. Even as the calf is sucking at her to get milk, she nudges it away; the calf must gain strength immediately to run if a lion comes for it. But what about a human? After thirty years most haven't built enough tenacity to overcome even the slightest troubles. Most are like the calf, begging for the mother's milk without first gaining the strength to stand. But as sure as the hungry lions do, troubles will soon come and destroy any bit of hope for the person who is not strong enough to overcome them."

He looked down at his mug and muttered to himself so that Agisillus hardly made out the strange words. "How long must I be among them before the poor fools learn to believe what they don't yet see?"

The man did not appear wealthy or noble. He was clothed more like the mountain men who trapped and came down to trade beaver, fox, or bear hides in the village, yet he spoke with authority. Even the Druids, who were considered by most people to be the wisest of all, never spoke so confidently and plainly about the gods and their relationship to humans like this man spoke about the one Creator. Agisillus had noticed how they liked to lean back and ponder, smoke their long-stemmed pipes and make a show of how observant and wise they were when discussing the things of the world. But their teachings were nebulous and their gods impersonal.

His father had taught him to learn as much as he could from the Druids about the earth and the stars and medicine but to be cautious of their teachings about the gods. This man was different. Like Agisillus's father, this man spoke of one God, the Creator, with conviction.

The stranger pinched his fingers under his nostrils and slowly spread them as he ran them along his mustache, straightening it again and again.

"What are man's limits?" he asked.

Agisillus shrugged his shoulders.

"Is it the body which his spirit is imprisoned to that puts limits on his strength and vitality?" the man went on.

"Is it the earth and all of its troubles and difficulties that make one a slave to his circumstance, so he's continually just keeping his head above water? Is it the wind, and the weather, the taxes, bad leaders, and the unfair wages . . . all those things that he likes to blame for his lack of success?

"Or perhaps it is in the mind where the seeds of purpose begin to turn to seeds of doubt?"

Agisillus thought the answer was clear; of course people were limited by their circumstances.

He hoped the man wasn't expecting a reply. Even the barkeep, who was adding a few logs to the fire, seemed to have his ear cocked for the answer.

The man waited.

Agisillus finally spoke.

"Who doesn't doubt themselves? When all you have in your hand is a hoe or a hammer like I did, you are limited, no matter how great of an idea you have. Even if you had a thousand great ideas, you still can do nothing unless the Creator wills it, and in my case, it is obvious he didn't."

The stranger leaned in, a sly smile straining his weather-beaten face. "So the Creator decides who succeeds and who doesn't? He decides that one farmer reaps a harvest and the other does not, even if both farmers equally toiled and sowed when it was time to sow?"

Agisillus glanced to his side hoping the barkeep was no longer within earshot and was glad to see he'd been called to another table. Being criticized by the stranger was one thing, but having an audience would be more humiliating.

He wished the stranger would keep his voice down.

"And what about the very things you mentioned now, the very tools you had in your hands, the hoe or the hammer. Could they in no way have been the answer to realizing that dream you had?" the man continued.

"Is a hammer not the tool one uses in the blacksmith shop to shape and mold? When you worked for the blacksmith, were you not in the very place you needed to be to create the tools you sketched?

"How about the hoe you used in the fields? Was it not that tool that gave you the inspiration for improving it?" The man leaned closer.

"If you desire to do great things, would the Creator not equip you also with the opportunities and appointments to settle this plan for you? Or do you think he is fiddling around with his creation, keeping people under his thumb like an evil child tortures an ant?"

Agisillus snorted and muttered, "It sure feels that way." He knew the man was right and so did the man, but he was hoping to divert the topic away from himself.

"He never plants a seed in the mind of a man without first orchestrating the journey he must take. When he plants a dream in a heart, he knows that if that person is not ready, the failures along the way can destroy every bit of hope and that person will never dream again. For some, it takes forty days to get through a desert: for others, it takes forty years.

"This is why he sets our feet on a journey. In order for this seed not to be choked by the misfortunes of life or the words of others, our mind must be cultivated. We must choose to overcome obstacles, over and over again, and never surrender. We must toughen our skin and become more tenacious. We must dig deep within ourselves until we find a reason to succeed so precious to us, that we never quit again. We must become masters over our fears and not be slaves of them.

"Just as a farmer cultivates his field by removing the rocks and clumps before he ever sets the seed into the earth, so must every person first work on removing those things from their life that can choke the growth of the seed.

"If the hammer and the hoe is all you had, then it's all you needed! Don't curse all you had!" He banged both hands on the table.

Agisillus pursed his lips as he remembered the time his father left him alone to till a portion of a field. He eventually got tired and instead of removing rocks, he spread dirt over them to hide them. A few months later there were empty patches in the corn rows, and the few stalks that grew were short and dry, hardly producing any corn. He would never forget the look of disappointment on his father's face when he confessed.

The man waved his hand toward Agisillus, as if he knew the moment the vagabond was reliving. "You see, the Creator will never be manipulated, because he is fair. He does not play favorites and reward one's work over another's. Each farmer will reap just as he has sown.

"But some people believe they will be rewarded and find success in their endeavors simply because they pray more than others. When it comes to the strength of their faith, of course they will be stronger if they pray more! If they pray for wisdom, of course they will gain wisdom! If they pray for peace and guidance, of course they will receive it! Those are gifts he grants freely to those who simply ask.

"But when it comes to finances, good health, good relationships, the things of the world he put us in control of, one must not be like the fools, believing they can reap what they have not sown, believing large satchels of money will be dropped in their laps if they only chant long enough and loud enough.

"Do you understand what I'm saying?"

Agisillus nodded.

"Hear me again: the Creator will not be manipulated. What kind of master will pay his servants an equal wage if one labors and the other sits on his rear end? An unfair one! Each must receive according to his labor; each must reap according to the measure they had sown.

"Sow seeds of doubt, fear, jealousy, hate, poverty, laziness, and they will overgrow your life like the weeds they are. They will choke any dream or vision you possess. And because they are weeds, they will always thrive wherever there is neglected soil! Weeds sprout rapidly, but a good harvest takes time and effort; this will always be the struggle of life. One must continually fight laziness, indifference, mediocrity, and fear to keep them at bay. Rest for too long, and the weeds start to creep back into the garden."

Agisillus stared at the table. "I understand that my life looks like a garden of weeds to you, but for a long time I truly did work hard," he said. "I wanted to prove everyone wrong for making me out to be a dreamer and an idler, and instead I proved them right. Do you know how humiliating it was to share ideas with people, only to see them glance at each other hardly containing their laughter? The more I revealed about myself, the more they had to gossip about. And when mother and father died . . ." Agisillus's voice choked. He struggled to finish the sentence and tried again. "When my parents died, those same 'friends' said I drove my parents to their grave."

The man nodded as Agisillus spoke and replied just as he

was done, "You tossed pearls before swine.

"You were searching for confirmation. You hoped they would convince you how great your idea was, and this would somehow give you confidence to proceed. You brought this dream to a people who don't even have their own dreams. A pig would not notice a pearl lost in its slop—it is only interested in more food. What does it care about pearls?"

Agisillus was just fine with the stranger calling the people back home *pigs*. But he still couldn't understand how they could be so satisfied with their monotonous lives.

The stranger seemed to have read his mind. "The dream was never meant for them. They grew up with you: why would they believe you could do anything different than they would? As far as they were concerned, you were cut from the same cloth, and your destiny was to be a farmer, too. It should never be your duty to impress people with all the things you *will* do."

Agisillus exhaled deeply and rested his cheek on his fist, staring into his mug.

"You are right. I should have kept my mouth shut until I actually achieved something first."

The man leaned back in his seat and crossed his arms, carefully scanning the tavern before he continued.

"Those who feel convicted of a calling will protect it from the opinions of others like a precious gem: working on it when no one is watching, keeping it in secret until the time is right for it to be revealed.

"Look at you, a healthy man, drinking the backwash of drunken warriors and begging strangers for a cup of beer. Instead of becoming that man who is respected and honored wherever he goes, you turned into a dog, eating scraps off the table of those less than you. You did prove them right!"

Agisillus's face turned bright red and his ears burned. He looked back at the fire, trying to conceal his humiliation.

His belly stung with the words just spoken, but words that would normally lead to a fight felt different coming from the stranger. There was a strange liveliness in his words. They were like arrows he had been dodging for a long time, but now each one found its target. They were arrows that pierced but were not meant to harm. Deep down he knew the man was speaking truthfully. It was as if the man knew his every fault and *still* saw potential.

He pulled his mug to his lips and swallowed what was left of the beer. He felt angry and trapped and seen and filled with hope—all at once.

"Is it not so? Are my words not the truth?" The stranger had noticed Agisillus's irritated shifting.

"Do not be offended by my words, they are not meant to humiliate you but to put some pride back into that pale chest of yours." He leaned across the table and gently thumped Agisillus on the chest with his fist.

"Do you know what the surest way to make a failure of a man is?"

He didn't wait for Agisillus to respond. "Just make him believe he is where he is by no fault of his own. Give a man the smallest of reasons for why he cannot succeed and he will make that reason his own. He will cling on to it dearly. It will come up in all his conversations. It will be his excuse to never try again and no one can take that away from him. Only the choice to succeed despite it can save him after that."

Agisillus fiddled with his mug, but the stranger put his hand on it and stopped him.

"You have much to see in this world, much to understand, and there is so much that you have not yet laid eyes on. There are empires out there you could not fathom.

"The empire now invading your land is one greater than man has ever seen. The walls, the aqueducts, the coliseums they construct are magnificent in size and beauty.

"Yet the great cities of this empire are not built in a day. There are principles the emperors, kings, and great minds of the world have long ago understood and used to store up their fortunes and bring forth their empires.

"These principles are displayed in all successful endeavors, in plain sight, yet people insist on calling them *secrets, luck, or God's favor.* Do you understand what I am saying?"

"Is that where you are traveling from . . . the empire?" Agisillus was glad the conversation had turned from him and assumed it was the Roman Empire the man was describing.

The stranger ignored him and continued, "People sit around fires and tell myths and legends of old, of men who conquered and men who shaped history as if these men possessed some extraordinary power. But they are romanticizing ordinary men who simply followed extraordinary principles.

"They never once think for a moment that they are just as capable."

Agisillus wanted to ask about the principles but was not about to open his mouth again. The more he did that the more the stranger revealed about him.

The stranger straightened, moved his mug to the side, and leaned in close to the young man.

"You might be surprised to know that the most profound wisdom comes from a farmer," the stranger said.

A farmer? What could kings and emperors learn from a farmer? Agisillus would have gladly taken advice on success from anyone in the world who would give it . . . anyone but a farmer. Then he thought of his father and the wisdom he'd attempted to share.

"Perhaps you should have been more observant when your father was toiling in the fields and you would see that it was not merely the work of his hands that produced the harvest."

"I know just about everything there is to know about farming," Agisillus quickly retorted. "We have been farmers for generations."

"So where does the seed come from that your father placed into the earth?" the stranger asked.

Agisillus's heart felt as if it were twisted in a knot as he remembered helping his father plant the seeds. He hated thinking of his father in that cursed field, working his final breaths away.

"Seeds come from a fruitful harvest," he finally responded.

The stranger nodded. "A seed is about as perfect a creation as nature has devised. When a seed is placed in cultivated soil, buried properly, it absorbs the minerals of the earth, the rays of the sun, and the rain, and then finally resurrects as a plant, which produces its own fruit and passes on a seed. Thus the seed has fulfilled the cycle, its purpose."

Agisillus nodded impatiently. He wondered why the man was talking to him about seeds. Of course he knew the process of a seed. There was nothing *profound* about it.

"*The proverbs of the diligent farmer* teach why *cultivation* of the soil must take place first. The soil is of course your heart and mind. They teach why you must then set time apart for *burial* of the seed after that. The seed, a gift of the Creator, is your dream. And if you truly let the Creator breathe life into your dreams, they will far surpass anything you could have imagined on your own.

"His imagination is certainly grander than yours." The stranger smiled and his eyes sparkled.

"Third, it is time for the *resurrection*. In due time, when the mind has been properly cultivated, the dream has been nourished, treasured, and toiled over, success is inevitable. "Finally, the mark of a truly successful person is left on the world when he not only reaps a bountiful *harvest*, but also leaves a seed, leaves wisdom or a legacy to pass on to others. Now this is a person that, like the seed, has completed the cycle and fulfilled their purpose."

Agisillus felt foolish for thinking the man was giving him a lesson in gardening. The man was simply using Agisillus's farming knowledge as a parable. Yet again he wished he had kept his mouth shut about knowing it all.

He straightened and cleared his throat. "How do I know which dream to follow? I've always had ideas, but what if I am putting energy toward something that was not destined for me?"

"What is the one dream you can't get out of your head?" the man asked. "Because that will be the one you regret not achieving if you quit."

"I don't know. It's been so long since I've thought about my dreams. Years ago my biggest dream was to free my mother and father from their work. Would it be so hard for the Creator to give a little guidance, perhaps a hint . . . or something that could help a person who is lost?"

The traveler did not answer him and instead, turned to look over his shoulder and then lowered his voice. "Look about you, these men are living at the bottom of the barrel and here you are also . . ."

Agisillus winced.

"You don't belong here, Agisillus." The wrinkles vanished

from the man's face, and his eyes widened as he leaned in and dropped his clenched fists on the table. His eyes darted left to right looking into each of Agisillus's eyes, as if he were begging, hopeful the vagabond would finally embrace his message.

"They have failed, they have quit on something they once dreamed of doing. And now they are trying to wash it all away. They settled, and now they are drifting through life, accepting what is lousy but at least familiar.

"These men are trying to suppress that dream so it never stirs them up again. But you can see it's eating at them. What once made them alive and vibrant, on fire, has cooled into a lukewarm existence. Their will to fail became stronger than their will to succeed. It's why they are sabotaging themselves, drinking their daily earnings away."

"The will to fail." Agisillus whispered the words under his breath, but the man heard him and paused. He said it again, "The will to fail . . . I am finding it hard to imagine this. I don't think I have ever met anyone who was willing to fail." Then he thought of himself and how he had lived the last two years of his life.

"Ask an old man if he wanted to fail or succeed, and he will never tell you he wanted to fail," said the traveler. "He will say the time was never right; the circumstances were impossible; the obstacles were much too difficult. He will say for other people, it was easier, and they had more opportunities . . . but for him it was not so.

"The will to fail is not a conscious decision, rather one that creeps in when a man is overcome by insecurity and believes he is not worthy of success. Every day a man must go to battle the moment he wakes in the morning. He must battle between choosing to take another step toward a dream, or to rest and plan on doing it tomorrow, postponing the possibility of success. It is especially debilitating to those who think very little of themselves and their abilities. They will secretly avoid taking action."

Agisillus remembered Cingetorix, who worked next to him at the blacksmith's shop. How he was constantly talking about needing more money but then complaining to Agisillus about the difficulty of his assignments. . . Did he have the will to fail?

And then about all the time he spent in the tavern back at the village—afraid to finally bring his invention to life, wallowing in self-pity. Had that been his will to fail?

He thought about the boys who once promised to take a trip with him to the next town over to find higher-paying work. But when he called on them one early morning, one by one they came out with reasons for why they could not go. Was that the will to fail in action?

"Agisillus, you had a great reason for why you wanted to succeed, but the *will to fail* showed its ugly face to you in the form of alcohol and sabotaged your life. It made you believe the gossip and lies. That *you* were somehow responsible for your tragedy and therefore you were not worthy of success, and you've been a slave to it ever since! You made a fool of yourself in your village. You quit on your dream. You not only lost your mother and father but you lost all of your dignity along the way . . ."

The man paused and grew silent.

He had noticed the vagabond wipe the hot tears dripping down his bony cheek. His short, tangled hair, which he had cut with a dull blade months ago, stuck out in every direction, and he patted it down with his palm, trying hard to hide his eyes.

The stranger's voice was soft and compassionate now as he dropped his wide shoulders.

"As difficult as it seems right now, this is a critical moment in your life," he said. "You are exactly where you need to be. If your life has not been bearing fruit, there is opportunity to grow.

"What happened before has passed; it is what you do going forward from this moment here that will dictate your life. Every day is an opportunity to begin anew, to choose a new path, to think and become different than you were the day before, to begin cultivating the soil of your mind.

"Don't waste another day waiting for people to see something in you before you believe in yourself. See it within yourself, and go live it!"

Agisillus nodded but kept looking down at the table. Laughter and conversations carried on around them as the two sat in silence. Agisillus finally gathered the courage to speak.

"I was going to kill myself tonight."

He struggled to keep from crying again.

The man leaned forward and squeezed Agisillus's shoulder. "Then it was no mistake I stopped here tonight. There are plans for you, young man. You have ears to listen, so hear this, Agisillus. Then I must be on my way."

The conversation Agisillus was hoping to avoid at the beginning of the evening was now one he desperately wished would not come to an end.

"In this age, very few have seen me as you see me now. Only to those whom I wish to encounter do I reveal myself. In another time and in another form, I will return, but that age has not yet come. And though many will come to know my name, I must first endure a trying journey. Some will hate me and call me blasphemer; others will follow me and call me teacher. You slept among the sheep; my time will begin among pigs in a manger. Those who desire to be used in great ways must first be humbled."

Agisillus lifted his eyes to look at the stranger. How did the stranger know where he last slept? Perhaps the stranger smelled him or noticed some of the sheep wool stuck to his trousers. And what did he mean by one day returning in another form? What an odd thing to say.

"Like you, I have committed myself to great things in the world." The man's eyes looked past the vagabond's shoulders to the fire pit. The flame danced in their reflection, and he seemed to disappear to another moment in time.

***

In the back of the tavern the musicians played their fiddle, the tune now somber and slow. The barkeep set refilled mugs next to the players; Agisillus assumed it was their payment for an evening of entertainment.

It was late, and the tavern was starting to empty. Some stumbled out alone and some clung to each other's shoulders to keep upright as they stepped into the snow. The barkeep circled the floor, collecting empty mugs off the tables and stacking them near the bar. He dipped each mug into a pail of water and flipped them upside down to dry.

He came close to where the two still sat and tossed another log onto the embers. Agisillus was thankful for it. He could hear the wind howl past that flap of fur in the door, and his heart filled with dread. Soon he too would have to step out into the cold once more.

He glanced at the giant man who remained silent, deep in thought.

The proverbs of the diligent farmer, he thought. The stranger spoke of them as if they had all the answers, yet he, too, has wandered into this tavern from the storm—what could he know about prosperity or success? What was he doing here at this late an hour?

Agisillus generally stayed in the shadows to avoid attention. Sometimes it was lonely not to receive a smile or a nod from someone passing by, but he preferred being ignored to the dirty looks he often received. His clothes were faded and torn. His hair grew in matted tangles. His leather shoes, with the strings that froze and broke, weren't going to last much longer.

But he wouldn't beg like the common vagabonds—the only difference between him and those who had made a lifestyle of it. They sat in the main roads with their hands stretched out to people passing by; he stayed in the alleyways, searching for discarded food the stray dogs hadn't found.

But this man looked him in the eyes, as if he were a normal human being, as if he were equal to any man in the tavern. The young man wished the conversation would never end. He finally broke the silence.

"I never heard of these proverbs from my father. He was the wisest man I knew and more open-minded than anyone in the village, but even he never spoke about them." Agisillus hoped the man would stay and keep talking. If this stranger believed he was capable of doing something extraordinary, perhaps he was.

"Common man will always remain common when he only thinks and acts on common things," the stranger replied. "Your father wanted you to learn this though he may not have heard of the proverbs himself—and although he might not have fulfilled all his dreams."

Agisillus nodded in agreement. It was true. He thought of

the villagers acting like a herd of sheep without a shepherd. If one person were overcome by fear, soon enough the entire village would be trembling. One person worried, and soon the entire village was scrambling to store food. Whether it was talk of war or the cold winter or disease, it didn't matter how good things were, people always tried to predict what disaster would happen next.

He thought of the time a man who proclaimed himself the best fisherman in the village came back empty-handed—and the entire village gathered to debate whether the lake was now empty of fish. Of course, the panic faded a week later when he again brought home a good catch.

When he began drifting from village to village, he noticed the people who had a unique approach to their craft seemed to be the most prosperous. Their approaches weren't common at all. The tavern with the liveliest entertainment was always filled to capacity. The fisherman who sold each fish as if it were his own pet always sold the most. The blacksmith who was willing to mold a custom request couldn't keep up with the orders.

But this was rare. Most people spoke the same, followed the same routines, and lived the same as everybody else and yet spent so much time complaining and cursing the very thing they spent their time on, the "common things," as the traveler had said. Everybody wanted to be successful. Everybody wished to have their taverns filled to capacity or their daily catch sold before the day's end, yet most people did nothing to change their luck.

Agisillus wondered if it was for this reason, this inability to dream and adapt, that the Romans now occupied the entirety of Gaul. They had no trouble overtaking this people with their massive armies and superior weaponry and shielding.

As he wandered, he once had the idea of finding work in one of the occupied towns, because every town with a Roman presence improved and grew. The markets flooded with trade goods from all over the world, the inns and taverns expanded to adjust for the influx of visitors and tradesmen. These towns seemed to have the widest roads, the deepest wells, and the most beautiful women.

He had a little experience with forging metal and thought he could learn the craft in a town like that. He even fantasized about finding someone who could be willing to help him mold one of his tool sketches. But the blacksmiths always turned him away. Perhaps it was the smell of alcohol or how frail he looked—they were never interested.

He didn't blame them—he *had* grown weak. The markets were only open in the day, making it hard to steal, so he rarely ate. His finest meals were the half-empty soup bowls left by patrons in taverns. With so little to eat and mostly beer to drink, his pants kept falling down, despite the string he'd tied around his waist to keep them up. His once-muscular forearms had veins protruding but were now scrawny and pale.

The traveler pushed his mug aside and slowly stood up. He looked at Agisillus with tenderness. The wrinkles on his forehead were arched and his head was tilted; it was a look he'd only seen once before, when his mother left him at school for the first time despite his objections.

Earlier in the evening, Agisillus had wanted nothing more than to be alone and to be warm. Now a lonely chill swept over him and a lump grew in his throat that he could not swallow away. Just a few hours ago he had nothing more to lose; now he felt like he was losing his only friend.

The man firmly grabbed Agisillus's shoulder. "Many times I've wandered into low places. But even in those places, I have never failed to find someone worth saving, someone thirsting for something more than the drink they clutch to. This conversation was no happenstance, Agisillus," he said, still holding the vagabond's bony shoulder.

"Remember the diligent farmer and remember that he is you."

Agisillus watched as the man spoke with the barkeep in a low voice for a few moments. He pulled open his fur coat, drew out a leather coin purse and set a few denarii on the bar. Both men turned to look at him near the fire, and he quickly looked away. He knew they were discussing his fate. Perhaps he would be allowed to stay near the fire for just a little longer. The traveler heaved his large rucksack to his shoulder, nodded at Agisillus, and then stepped out into the cold.

He was gone.

Chapter 4
The First Scroll: Cultivation

"You may have stumbled into a little bit of luck tonight, boy." The barkeep had walked up to Agisillus unnoticed. "Your friend left a few extra denarii on your behalf. Said you could use another beer and a place to sleep tonight. There is a bit more stew left; I will bring you a bowl."

In a few minutes he set a steaming bowl in front of the vagabond. Agisillus's stomach growled as the smell hit his nostrils. He waited until the man walked away before grabbing the spoon with his trembling hand and carefully bringing it to his mouth.

He cried without making a sound as he swallowed each

spoonful. The hot stew, thick with some sort of meat, which he guessed was lamb, filled his belly and his soul. He made every little bit of the chunky goodness last as long as he could.

Later, the barkeep led him through the back room past a large stone chimney. They crawled up a ladder to a loft just above. The man lit a candle on a small table and illuminated a bed of straw with a cowhide spread across it. Agisillus almost wept with gratitude—it had been so long since he'd slept in a proper bed. The chimney made the tiny room toasty. As they both crouched to walk underneath the low ceiling, the planks creaked with each step.

The tavern had not looked very big from the exterior but from the vantage point of the loft it proved to be much more spacious. The supporting beams stretched from the middle post to the top of the circular outside walls, and the whole thing looked like a massive cart wheel lying on its side. The thick middle post ran from the ground up to the top of the roof, and reeds supported the straw bundles layered to protect the tavern from the elements.

From the loft Agisillus could see down into the rest of the bar, where he'd sat by the fire, and into another room he assumed was the barkeep's.

"You can stay here tonight," the barkeep said as he pulled up a corner of the fur bedding and pushed some loose straw back into the pile with his foot. "Tomorrow, I'll ask you to continue on wherever it is you were headed."

Agisillus nodded and whispered, "Thank you." He stretched his right hand toward the man. The barkeep's bushy brows went up with a look of surprise, and he shook the extended hand. Such a well-mannered gesture from a lowly vagabond was unexpected. He studied the young man for a moment and combed his fingers through his long beard which reached the top of the apron draped around his neck.

He turned and climbed down the ladder, his bald head disappearing into the room below, but a few moments later crawled back into the loft. In his hand was a rolled scroll with a cut of leather wrapped around it, holding it together. A leather string decorated with a blue bead was tied in a knot to keep it secure. He handed it to Agisillus.

"Your friend left it for you as he was paying for your stay."

He hesitated for a moment with his hairy hands on his hips before he spoke again, perhaps curious to see if Agisillus would open it right away. "I hadn't planned on giving it to you. Whatever it contains appears to be valuable, I wanted to see what it was. I didn't think a drifter would make much use of it."

Agisillus held the wrapped scroll in both hands unsure of what to say.

"Forgive me if I speak honestly, but I see men like you walk into this tavern every day looking for a drink or food you have no intention of paying for. I was glad when that friend of yours stepped in—I don't enjoy throwing men out into the cold. I hope he didn't make a mistake giving this to you. He said it contains a few of life's greatest treasures . . . Seems like you could use some."

***

Agisillus tugged the cart up a steep slope in the road. He was thankful that snow had melted weeks ago, but the rainfall that followed had left the roads muddy and impossible to walk on, let alone pull the heavy load of supplies.

He had not counted the days but knew it had already been a month, maybe more, that he'd lived in the loft of the tavern. Several times in the evenings he would start to untie the knot around the old leather but always stopped short of unrolling it.

He was afraid to open it. Whatever treasures or riches the parchment may have promised, how could it ever solve his troubles or feed him? Besides, he was not ready to start dreaming of riches again; he was determined to first show the world he wasn't lazy and was capable of earning his keep.

He thought back to that first night in the tavern. That night he slept longer than he had ever slept in his life. It was already the evening of the next day before he had crawled down out of the loft, awoken by the noise of the regulars entering the bar for their nightly drink.

He was prepared to leave but when he helped the barkeep lift a large barrel onto the table, the man poured him a large mug of beer and then another. He then pushed a bowl of stew in front of him. Agisillus couldn't remember how he got his hands on the next several beers after that but eventually stumbled out into the snow and leaned against the old tavern wall to shelter him from the howling wind. He thought about the warm loft but could not bring himself to beg the barkeep to allow him to stay a second night.

Across the snow-covered road he saw a man carrying an armful of wood toward his hut. As the man pushed through the door, Agisillus squinted to focus his drunken eyes and see inside of the hut. A woman hurried to help the man carry the wood to the fireplace. Hanging over the roaring fire was a cauldron from which steam was rising. The woman smiled at her husband as she stirred the evening dinner.

A small child appeared in the doorway and stared through the snow at the drunk man huddled against the wall of the tavern. He waved at Agisillus, and then the door was shut.

The traveler's question echoed in his mind, "Don't you have children to tuck in, a fire to keep lit through the night, a hut to protect from the cold?"

The words haunted him.

His head began to spin. He dropped on his hands and vomited every bit of beer and stew on to the snow. He leaned back against the tavern, ready to die. The barkeep found him hours later and dragged his unconscious body back into the tavern.

That next morning when he crawled down from the loft, head throbbing and confused as to how he got there, the barkeep slapped him so hard on the cheek that he stumbled to the ground.

"You fool!" the bald man snarled as he stood over him. "I should have let you die there in the snow and buried you like a stray dog. It is not my responsibility to take care of you, but if you can't control yourself when you drink, then maybe its best you don't touch the stuff again. You're too young to die, boy, but that's what is in store for you. Do something with yourself—I am embarrassed for you."

Agisillus touched his cheek at the memory and continued to tug the cart down the road. It wasn't the first time in these last few years that he'd taken a beating, but this one seemed to stick. The words of the barkeep played in his mind constantly, and he thought of the traveler, too. He was lucky to have stumbled into the tavern on that night. Both men had spoken harshly but told him exactly what he needed to hear. Just like his father who spoke to him that way on several occasions when he would complain or play victim, never withholding a truthful word, yet remaining genuine and caring.

He and the barkeep had made an agreement. He could stay in the loft in exchange for lending a hand around the tavern and keeping the supplies stocked. And Agisillus swore he would never drink again.

He didn't understand why the barkeep had been so kind, but he was willing to work hard to stay in his good graces. Once a week he pulled the cart to the oceanside town miles away, often heading out in the dark hours of the morning to make it back by evening. He purchased fresh barrels of beer, meats, and preserved vegetables and loaded the cart. It could only handle two barrels and a few sacks of vegetables and wheat at a time, so he had to make the trip often.

The barkeep had introduced himself as Vectimarius, but Agisillus still called him sir. Every evening he collected water into the cauldron and helped his new boss slice up vegetables and peel potatoes for the stew they served to the tavern customers. He ran around between the patrons in the evenings and made sure every mug was filled with beer as soon as it had been emptied, so often craving a sip for himself but never allowing himself to take one. One always led to two. He would not take the chance.

His favorite nights were when a musician would play in the tavern. He sat near the fire and watched the magic happen as the musician and his fiddle became one. The whine of the fiddle often brought up old memories, and he fought hard not to cry. Every night, when the last man finally stumbled out, he stacked the chairs and benches onto the tables and swept the floor with the straw broom before he headed up to his warm loft.

With a place to sleep and food in his belly, he felt like a human once again. It was good to work hard, to be a part of society, and to be useful.

How quickly I felt worthless when I became idle, he thought. *Even if I ever pursue my dream again, I will never quit my everyday work until I can afford to; never again.*

It was the constant anticipation and hope for a breakthrough that had kept him slacking at the blacksmith shop in the first place. He was sure any day someone would agree his inventions were a fantastic idea and help him create them.

But once he was kicked out from the shop, the time spent not working at all slowly eroded his belief in himself, and he began to believe he was as lazy as people had said he was. But now good fortune had finally paid him a visit.

For the first time in what seemed like years, Agisillus exhaled. He felt strong and the long walk for supplies allowed for time to reflect.

Maybe he would finally open the scroll when he got back to the tavern.

***

The old leather was dark and discolored. It looked to be a thousand years old, and the worn edges of the parchment were soft to the touch. It had not lost its smell—leather never did—Agisillus noticed as he put it to his nose.

He carefully untied the knot in the middle and pulled the strings to the sides. He moved the candle to the floor next to the scroll to get a better look. Lying on his belly, he propped himself up on his elbows and began unrolling the leather.

The length of each parchment was the same as the distance from the tip of his fingers to his elbow. The large pieces curled as if they had not been opened for a long time, and he pulled the corner of the first one back to count four pieces of the yellowed material.

The writing on scrolls was as beautiful, neat, and orderly as he'd ever seen. He slowly moved his finger along the large text at the top of the first scroll. *The proverbs of the diligent farmer*, he read slowly.

The Druids had taught Agisillus and all the other boys to read Latin. His mother would wrap a dried fish and a piece of bread for him in a cloth sack, and they would walk together to school, where she would leave him and go to the market. Boys from three or four other villages gathered there as well, and the ones from the larger villages were loud and behaved like savages. He enjoyed watching the old Druid silently float up to one of them in his long white tunic and slap their hands with a switch.

While the language was hard to learn, it was law to read and write in Latin, and the Druids were forced to teach it because of the Roman conquest. He hated Latin; it was foreign and ugly to him and always felt silly when the Druid would make the children shout in unison, sounding each letter out, and write it with the red berry dye on the marble tablets.

One night, he washed the dye off the tablet and told his mother that he wished his father had killed more Romans during the battles so he wouldn't have to learn Latin. She told him to never say such words out loud again.

Now, he was happy to have the ability to decipher this language.

The ladder creaked loudly as the barkeep poked his head into the loft, carefully lifting a full mug of beer and setting it on the floor at the entrance.

"You've worked hard these last few months, boy. I just tapped the new keg you brought in." He slowly slid the mug toward Agisillus and stared at it for a moment.

"You haven't asked for a single drop, and I am very pleased to see that you have practiced some self-control. You deserve this one." With that, his bald head disappeared to the floor below.

Agisillus reached for the mug and pulled it next to him. He had been craving a drink, as he served beer and dragged barrels behind him in the wagon, but hated how the alcohol made the old memories come flooding back in. But things were looking up now. Maybe he was safe. He took a long sip of the beer and pulled the first scroll apart from the other three.

The Proverbs of the Diligent Farmer

To the reader who seeks wisdom, prosperity, and truth: May these truths be etched in his mind, all the days of his life.

Scroll 1 The Cultivation

1:1 The diligent farmer knows that long before the seed can be planted, the field must be prepared. He clears the trees, removes the roots, and establishes clear boundaries.
The wise seek clarity for what they desire. They set boundaries, are disciplined, and approach each day with intention. Fools wish for many things, but without a clear path they do not see the pit. They stumble and fall in their search for happiness.

1:2 The diligent farmer rises early and heads to the fields. He examines the work of the previous day and makes note of where he needs to correct his irrigation.
The wise rise early to examine their life with a fresh mind. Fools love sleep and never correct their ways.

1:3 The diligent farmer does not envy the harvest of his fellow farmer. When he sees it, he is inspired and believes he is also capable of gathering such a harvest.
The wise have come to believe they are equal among all men. All things are possible to those that believe. They begin at once to work for those things which are possible. Fools keep a jealous eye on the success of others and become blind with envy to their own possibilities.

1:4 The diligent farmer purchases the diaries of farmers, merchants, and the wealthy that came before him. He reads of their success and fills his mind with visions of his own prosperity. As he learns their ways, his wisdom grows and his fields benefit. He keeps his mind free of the circus in the village as other farmers gather to distract themselves after a day's toil.
The wise invest in a library—they are students of those they admire and came before them. Fools spend their wages in taverns or at the platforms of street performers. They distract themselves from a worthy future; they are lovers of entertainment and haters of discipline.

1:5 The diligent farmer sifts through the soil and plucks rocks from his field because they will hinder the growth of any seed planted nearby.
The wise examine their thoughts. They uncover beliefs that may hinder their destiny and they pluck them out. Fools become inspired and have many ideas, but soon their dream perishes in the doubt

and insecurity which was never removed from their mind.

1:6   The diligent farmer walks the field and dashes his hoe against the clumps of hardened dirt until they crumble.
The wise prepare their minds for new possibilities; they reflect on life and examine where they may have become hardened. They break old habits and develop favorable ones. Fools live in the past; they blame their ancestors, their circumstances, and their old wounds. They conclude change is impossible and become hardened all the more.

1:7   The diligent farmer leaves his field in the evening and makes his way to the prosperous man who has stored up a great harvest. He sits around the fire and does not speak; he only listens to the wisdom of the successful farmer and takes note. He learns what he must do in the winter, how he must prepare in the fall, what he must plant in spring, and how to reap in the summer.
The wise treasure mentors they can imitate. Fools idolize royalty and celebrity.

1:8   While the diligent farmer may experience failure, he still spends hours seeing in his mind that which he wants to become and have. By candlelight, he continues to draw plans for the storehouses he will one day fill.
The wise have resolved never to surrender their dreams, no matter how difficult the journey may be. The difficulties they face prepare them for greatness. Fools are destroyed by difficulty. Life for them is nothing but misery; they believe life is working against them.

1:9   The diligent farmer lies awake long into the night, losing sleep in his angst over who he must become.
The wise gladly accept restlessness which comes when one must leave comfort and safety. Fools drown in anxiety that comes when one has no purpose or direction.

1:10 The diligent farmer stands over the dormant field in the evening, he wipes the sweat from his brow, and he does not enter his hut until in his mind he sees the fruitful crops, the workers gathering the produce and filling the storehouses, and the harvest from all of his labor.

The wise understand they must see in their mind's eye what they desire, until that which they desire becomes a part of who they are. They live as if they are already in possession of it without doubt in their heart. Fools live in fear and worry, they sow discord in their own heart, and soon they come to possess that which they feared, and they are perplexed.

1:11 The diligent farmer observes how all of nature responds to the words he speaks and is gentle in the words he chooses. He speaks not of what is but of how he desires it to be. He does not curse the dry soil; he does not curse the blue sky. When his thoughts become angry or full of hate, fear, and worry, he opens his mouth and drowns out his thoughts with words of affirmation, peace, joy, and prosperity. He understands that when the seed is planted, it will only thrive in surroundings that are life-giving.

Life comes from the mouths of the wise, and they create prosperity with it. Fools breathe hate, fear, gossip, and worry—and death comes to their bones and everything their hands touch.

1:12 The diligent farmer may hear rumors of changing seasons, droughts, and the dropping value of crops. He does not become discouraged or sell his land like the other farmers. He does not seek employment elsewhere like his anxious peers. Because he is not stricken with panic, he will soon be rewarded for his persistence.

The wise do not follow the herd; they know it is folly to conform. They stay true to their unique purpose. Fools are like a leaf in the wind; they float whichever way the wind blows and find themselves in old age never having planted anything worthwhile.

1:13 The diligent farmer dines with his friends who consume strong drink and gather the courage to criticize his dreams. They cast the limitations of their own experiences and failed endeavors onto him. They say, "It is impossible in this village," and "Not all can be rich." But he does not argue with them and makes way to his still-dormant field in the moonlight to ponder.

The wise do not entertain the limitations of others or walk in the footsteps of fools. Like drunkards who stumble on the stones in the road, fools stumble on the words of others; they let the words of others shape their decisions. Soon, they will hate themselves, their lives, and their critics.

1:14 The diligent farmer makes his way to the fields of a good and wealthy man. He finds him toiling and helps the man prepare his field. He studies his ways and learns all that he can. On his way home he passes the barren field of the poor farmer, who is resting in the shade with his hands folded on his chest. The poor farmer says, "Let us share stories now, tomorrow we will begin the work," but the diligent farmer spends no time with him.

The wise make friends of those they want to imitate. Fools make friends of those without ambition.

1:15 The diligent farmer walks past the harvest of others, and when his eyes see their success, he becomes inspired all the more.

Big ideas are planted into the mind of the wise, and their ambitions stretch when they see new possibilities. Fools think little, believe little, and receive little because their mind is fed with little.

1:16 The diligent farmer is eager to plant the seed, but he knows there is still work that needs to be done so he gets busy.

The wise eagerly await ideas and inspiration and trust God's timing, but they do not simply wait. They continue to gain wisdom, they do not sit idle, and when an opportunity strikes, they act immediately. Fools sit with their hands folded and find misery wherever they turn. They say, "I am waiting on the Lord," but idle hands and feet only bring poverty and confusion.

1:17 The diligent farmer studies the leaves of the trees and notices when they turn color. He remembers the season that passed and knows that the next will pass just as quickly. He visits with the old people in the village and hears their stories of regret. He hurries back to his fields and gets to work, aware that precious time is passing.

The wise think often to the end of their days, bringing urgency to how they live today. Fools love the idea of "Tomorrow," but soon they will rip at their hair and plead the heavens for one more "Today."

1:18 In the evening, the diligent farmer lights a torch and writes all he did that day. He notices routines. He makes note of the hours wasted, the moments of distraction, and thoughts that were negative. He sees all he can do to correct his way.

The wise observe their habits and correct their ways. Fools are like a lost man in the forest, passing by the same tree over and over, desperately seeking a way out but refusing to change course.

1:19 The diligent farmer notices the way a wealthy man carries himself. The way he speaks, the way he walks, the way he girds his waist, the way he stops to think. The diligent farmer straightens his back, lifts his chin, and does the same.

The wise embody what they desire to be. Fools mock what they can't be and scoff at what they cannot achieve.

1:20 The diligent farmer builds a fence around his fields. As he is digging holes and placing posts, he whispers to himself. He is like a crazy man when others see him, but he knows that if he stops speaking words of life out loud, his thoughts of fear will take back their residence in his mind. Instead, his mind has no choice but to repeat back to him that which he has spoken over his life, and he has changed his thinking. He knows that a negative thought is loud in the mind but even an audible whisper will defeat it.

The wise change their thoughts by drowning out thoughts of fear with loud words of power, faith, and vision. Fools cower in silence under thoughts of fear, worry, and indecision, and their life is shaped by these thoughts.

1:21 The diligent farmer prepares for bed in the evening, and when he has bathed he stands looking at the wall of his hut. On it he has hung sketches, words of encouragement, and plans he has for the future. The wall is covered by these things, and he is reminded once again of where he is going. They are the last thing he sees before he falls asleep and the first thing he sees when he arises.

The wise keep a diary of their dreams. Fools keep a satchel of excuses.

1:22 The diligent farmer has prepared his fields. The land has been cleared of brush and trees, the field has been measured and staked, the land has been tilled, the rocks have been removed, the soil has been fertilized, the clumps have been broken, and the fence has been built. The diligent farmer has cultivated his land. He is ready to bury the seed.

The wise have prepared their body, hearts, and minds to receive inspiration and opportunities that will bring about their purpose. Fools do no such work and go through life without happiness, wealth, or meaning.

Those with eyes to see and ears to hear, let them see and hear!

Agisillus stared at the scroll. It was late. The logs had long ago turned to hot coals.

His mug was empty at his side. He thought about a refill

but was hesitant to ask; the barkeep had been pleased with his self-control. He pulled the corner of the scroll back to see the second scroll marked "Scroll 2" but did not continue with it. He had much to ponder and quietly climbed down the ladder to add wood to the fire.

He sat and poked at the coals to revive the flames. "*The Proverbs of The Diligent Farmer*," he whispered. What was his "seed"? What was he supposed to have done with his life, before everything fell apart? The proverbs were revealing. It bothered him that his life resembled the fool's more than the wise man's.

For weeks, Agisillus mulled over the scroll as he worked. Every night, when his daily chores were finished, he headed for his loft, carefully unrolled the first scroll, and read through it again and again. He was determined not to read the next one until he could completely grasp the writings of the first one.

Some of the proverbs were obvious—philosophies he had heard before and even believed in. Others, he had to reread many times. The proverbs emphasized the importance of the mind and thoughts of the diligent farmer over his physical labor.

They urged a man to work hard but more importantly, to have his thoughts in order. They warned of contradictions in the mind; no matter what a man wanted, what he thought about most would guide his ways.

But wasn't it this exact kind of thinking that had caused him to lose everything in the first place? As much as he'd dreamed of a better life for his parents, as much as he'd dreamed of wealth, those dreams were always followed by a little voice that reminded him of his limitations.

He could imagine success when he closed his eyes but when he opened them, he only saw the untilled fields, the parched earth, and his parents' calloused hands. Could a person really dream with his eyes open and not be discouraged by his current circumstances?

If the proverbs in the scroll were to be taken as truth, what else could he have done to better prepare the "soil," to better prepare for opportunities?

He knew he could not live in the tavern forever; it was only a matter of time until he would need to move on. But how? And where? He feared if he allowed his mind to start dreaming again, he could end up in the same mess he was in before. Perhaps it would be better to hold off reading the rest of the scrolls . . . for now.

Chapter 5
The Second Scroll: Burial

Agisillus anxiously increased his pace. He was further south than he had ever gone before. Up north, where the pureblooded Gauls remained, most villages were alike. If he visited one for the first time, it would still feel familiar to him. People were laid back—slow about their tasks, never in much of a hurry—they even seemed to speak slowly. There was always a tavern, an inn, and the shops of craftsmen and tradesmen on either side of a main street.

There were times he would get drunk in the tavern of one village and wake up in an alley of another. He would only later come to realize he was in a different village than the one he started out in.

This large town, Gorgiva, however, bustled with energy and was unlike anything he'd seen before. There were three-story buildings towering over him. He noticed every inn had a balcony above the ground floor, and most of the straw roofs had been remodeled with red clay shingles. Agisillus admired the Roman-inspired architecture.

But the street performers on stilts made him nervous; their masks reminded him of the creatures he'd seen in a bad dream once. There were people everywhere, and the busyness overwhelmed him. The roads were wide, and horse-drawn carriages forced pedestrians to jump aside as their hooves clicked by.

He pulled his cart to the side as a Roman patrol marched through, footsteps perfectly in sync, armor clinking with each step. The men stared straight ahead with chins up and serious faces.

He heard rumors that the further south one went, the more one could find Gauls who had become Roman citizens. When the wars ended, many soldiers had settled in the territory. Sometimes Gaul women would even marry Romans.

After Agisillus had carved a sign near the main road, pointing into the village, the Watering Hole had become a favorite stop for travelers. Vectimarius wanted to expand his business and created a menu that required more rare spices and grains. This meant Agisillus needed to shop much further south, where only certain towns had access to merchant ships for supplies.

The barkeep had given him a set of used trousers and a tunic to replace his torn clothes, but they were much too big for his skinny body and the trousers sagged around his rear end. The new sandals fit nicely, and he was thankful for the summer footwear. He also received a sack of food and money for the long trek, and the pieces of silver jingled with every step the entire way.

Hundreds of times along the way he had peeked into the sack to make sure he hadn't lost any coins. When he first looked in, he was surprised to spot the old leather of the parchment. The barkeep must have slipped it in the bag before he headed out.

With a few coins budgeted for lodging, Agisillus looked for an inn. He could use solitude from all of the excitement of the town. In the morning he would buy the supplies from his list and begin the journey back to the village.

The sky was ablaze—its red clouds painted by the setting sun seemed to be frozen in place when he stepped out of the inn. The streets were mostly empty of the earlier busybodies; only a few men chatted further down the cobblestone street. The occasional distant barking of dogs broke the silence of the peaceful evening.

He had the sack slung over his shoulder and clung to it tightly. Large towns had pickpockets, and he did not trust anyone.

When he had first checked in, he spotted a tavern from the window and now headed across the street toward it. The inn had cost him less than the lodging budget, and he discovered a few spare coins. He craved a beer and knew it would ease the tension. Things were going well, and besides, he would only have one.

The modest tavern was squeezed by taller buildings on either side of it, as if the proprietor had refused to advance when the rest of the town had expanded. Its stone walls and clay mortar were noticeably older than the three-story structures looming over it. Torches burning on either side of the doorway illuminated the shiny coin in his palm.

He feared exposing the money in his sack when paying for a drink—it would make him an easy target in a strange town—so he prepared the coin before he walked in. He pulled his trousers up at the waist and stepped inside.

Familiar smells of beer and wet rags instantly filled his nostrils. There were only a few tables inside the snug room, and each table was furnished with several stools and a candle the size of a man's head. The wick, burning for hours at a time, had melted the candles to the tabletops, dripping hot wax down to the wood before cooling and sticking the candle to the surface. *Either a clever or a sloppy way to avoid using a candle holder*, Agisillus thought. The wax spread and filled the crevices where drunken men had carved their names into the tables.

A few men spoke in low voices at the far end of the room next to where the barkeep was sweeping the plank floor. At the back wall, several logs burned in the fireplace. Agisillus wanted to sit at the table next to it but settled for a seat next to the door, further from the other men. After all his time exposed to the elements, he could never quite get enough of a nice warm fire, even if it were summer. He never took it for granted. He settled himself on the three-legged stool and stretched his legs around the old wine barrel that had been repurposed as a table.

He held the beer with both hands and glanced at his sack on the floor. The parchment poked out, the worn leather almost shining in the candlelight. He wondered what his father would make of it. Would such a wise man and farmer find the proverbs accurate and true?

He thought of the strange traveler who had given it to

him on that cold miserable night. It seemed so long ago
when he had first stepped into the tavern, just hours away
from concluding to end his life. He shivered at the
thought of it. The man had stepped into his life at just the
right moment, and perhaps he owed it to him to at least
study all four scrolls.

"Whatever a man sees in his mind, does not doubt in his
heart, and lives as if he has already received, will come to
pass." The stranger had whispered it before he stood up
to leave, as if it were a secret.

"So instead of just wishing, begin to give thanks for that
which you desire, and it will be God's good pleasure to
give it to you."

Agisillus chuckled sarcastically but quickly lowered his
head to take a sip when the other men in the tavern
turned to look at him. He talked to himself so often that
sometimes he laughed or smirked out loud without
realizing it.

The traveler's "secret" was a good thought, a well-
meaning idea, but was it not precisely what he had already
done when he was dreaming of riches and freedom for
his father and mother? Every day he imagined creating his
farming tools, selling them all throughout the land and
being rich. Why hadn't this "secret" worked for him
then? And there was no example in the proverbs of the
diligent farmer for how a wise man lives, even when he
has lost everything.

He wrestled with the familiar memories. He saw his
mother and father in the field and quickly brushed the
thought aside. He remembered the sketches and curled
his nose in disgust. Then he saw the faces of the villagers
as their looks turned from sympathy, then to pity, and
finally to blame over the years as he transformed from a
boy, to an orphan, to a drunkard.

He reached into the sack, pulled the parchment apart, and carefully smoothed the scrolls.

The barkeep walked over to offer his newest patron another round. Agisillus hesitated and looked down at the sack. He would probably have enough in the budget for one more and nodded.

He wished the traveler were here now—he had questions about the proverbs. Perhaps he had not properly "cultivated" his field before he tried planting his seed. Perhaps the ideas came to him, but he had not learned anything about the business of manufacturing tools.

Perhaps he should have consulted with the blacksmith and learned what it would take to manufacture one of his inventions. Where would the metals come from, and who supplied them to the shop? How much would they need to melt down, and how long would it take to mold one? Would there even be enough farmers in his village who would buy his tools from him? How far would he need to travel to reach more customers? And even if he created it, would he even know how to sell it?

He remembered sitting at the lake, dreaming of being rich and helping his parents and how badly those very dreams had crushed his spirit. His closest friend had scoffed, "I just hope you're generous enough to lend me a few denarii when you're sitting atop your money pile."

They cast the limitations of their own experiences and failed endeavors onto him. They say, "It is impossible in this village," and "Not all can be rich." But he does not argue with them . . .

Agisillus ran his finger over the text and read it again. He wished he had kept his mouth shut and let people see his actions. Maybe he should have come to a large town like this one first and shared his sketches with a blacksmith here.

A blacksmith in a town like this one would take him

seriously, and he would not know of Agisillus's humble background. In his own little village, no one was a stranger, so why wouldn't they mock him? He had never done anything that would make them believe it. No one had ever done anything like it before.

The fresh beer was set at the corner of the table, and Agisillus leaned over to pull it closer. He carefully moved the first scroll to the bottom and straightened the scroll marked "2."

Scroll 2 The Burial

2:1   The diligent farmer sees his fellow farmers scatter seeds on the rocky ground and the birds of the air eat them up. He sees them scatter seeds near shrubs that were not removed and the seeds suffocate. He sees them scatter seeds in shallow soil and the plants never take root. He offers advice, but they do not take it, they only hope for a quick harvest. He pities them, because the diligent farmer knows that anyone could come into possession of precious seed, but only the seed buried in good soil will ever produce a harvest.

The wise, when they have been given a dream, take hold of it and plant it deep into their minds and hearts and believe it is possible for them before they have even spoken of it. They begin to work toward it before it is trampled by fear, doubt, and indecision. Fools shout their plans from the rooftops for the entire world to hear before any action has been taken, but soon their dream dies out. It was tossed to the wind, scattered on rocky ground, and shallowly planted. It never stood a chance.

2:2   The diligent farmer comes home from toiling in the field; he closes the door of his hut, drops to his knees and cries out. He is becoming divided in his mind. Around him, he sees all the work that still has to be done, but in his mind he continues to see his dream as if it were fulfilled. His dream is real and yet so distant. Later he gathers himself off of the ground and wipes his tears. He remembers that a seed must first be buried before it can rise as a plant and bear fruit.

The wise endure pain in their search for more. They know even the darkest hours can't kill true purpose. Fools run from pain and settle for less; they complain to all who would listen and get drunk on sympathy. They discover no purpose.

2:3 The diligent farmer knows the seed is a gift from his creator. He understands that in order for this gift to bear fruit, he must invite the gift-giver into a partnership. He understands that he does not hold the sun in his hands and cannot pull rain from the clouds; he cannot squeeze nutrients from the soil nor minerals from water to nourish his seeds. He does not hold the seed tight in fear of losing it. He buries it in faith that it will bear fruit.

The wise receive their dreams and ideas as if they were from God, they pursue them as such and they prosper. Fools say, "There is no God," and their dreams turn to vanity. Their lives are desolate and bear no fruit. Their money brings no happiness. Their hearts have little empathy. Their possessions are a burden. Even large meals do not satisfy their hunger.

2:4 The diligent farmer is not impressed by fancy talk at the dinner table. He does not become discouraged by those who attempt to be superior. He knows that greatness is achieved by those who have calloused hands and are eager to work, eager to sow, eager to live.

The wise have come to know that extraordinary things are done not by those who are exceedingly intelligent, talented, or spiritual; they are rather done by men and women with a dream to live for. Fools are intimidated by the crafty and excuse themselves from greatness. They are given the gift of life, but they have little to hope for. Soon, the boastful and the foolish will look upon the wise with jealousy.

2:5 The diligent farmer knows that merely receiving the seed will not bring him a harvest and riches. He wakes in the morning and goes right to work, planting his seed. While his clothes may be torn, his feet bare, and his purse empty, he does not mind, because now he has the seed, and when it bears fruit, he will purchase everything he needs.

The wise have come to understand that a man with nothing in his possession but a dream is wealthier than one who has worldly possessions but no purpose. They know that for a man with a dream, all things are possible, so they take hold of their dream. Fools seek luxury, fine clothes, and fancy meals, and they even accrue debt for these things, but they are never satisfied.

2:6 The diligent farmer comes home after long hours in his fields and his spirit is weary, but he remembers the seeds he has planted in the field, and he becomes alive once again. He has hope and it revives him.

The wise become alive by their dreams, ambitions, and desires. Fools lack enthusiasm. They have nothing to fight for, to live for, or to breathe for.

2:7 The diligent farmer tends to his fields. While the seeds are still below the ground, he watches for weeds and plucks them, he keeps the birds of the air from his soil, he prays for rain and for sunshine, and all these things bring him closer to the days of reaping the harvest.

The wise continue to work on their dreams even when progress cannot be seen; they are not fooled by the seed which has not yet broken through the ground, and they know they must only persist. Fools believe simply having an idea will make them rich, and when nothing comes of it, they move on to another.

2:8 The diligent farmer stands in the field and wipes the sweat from his brow. He rests and ponders all he has done. He watches over his field with a careful eye and gains new perspective—he sees where he must mend the fence and where the soil is eroding, and he gets to work.

The wise understand that they can work themselves to death and still miss opportunity. They know that when the way is clear, they can work diligently, but when the way becomes unclear, they must step back and find clarity. Fools keep busy with pointless tasks and life becomes a cycle with no end in sight. They busy themselves right out of opportunity.

2:9 The diligent farmer hears the excitement of other farmers in the market. The seeds they buried have broken ground and plants are sprouting from the soil; they are filled with joy. Yet he does not become discouraged; he does not ask himself why he has not seen growth; he does not become disheartened or jealous. Instead he congratulates them and goes about his business.

The wise are never discouraged by the success of others; rather they are encouraged all the more. Fools throw their hands in the air, shake their heads, and say, "It will never be me!"

2:10 The diligent farmer wakes early and tends to his fields. When he is done, he does not rest; he draws out a stone and begins to sharpen his hoe and his scythe. It is not yet time for harvest, but he makes himself ready.

The wise never wait to ready themselves; long before opportunity comes, they are working on their craft. Fools never sharpen their tools, and rust begins to show. Opportunity falls through their fingers while they are scrambling in the final hour.

2:11 In the market, the diligent farmer begins to make deals with the merchants. He agrees on prices and timelines. He counts the number of trips it will take for the delivery cart to transport all of his harvest. He firmly shakes hands with the merchants, and as he walks away, they look at each other and nod. Here is a businessman they look forward to dealing with.

The wise act as if they are already in possession of their dream, and their body, mind, and soul take on a new identity. Once their mind has received orders on how to think, how to carry itself, how to feel, it is only a matter of time until it brings to them exactly that which it was led to believe. Fools lead their mind to believe in scarcity, lack, and poverty. They breathe shallowly, shake hands weakly, lack confidence, and few want to do business with them.

2:12 The diligent farmer remembers that even though the soil first appears to be a grave for the little seed, the seed must be laid down in order to grow. What appears to be a grave will soon become an incubator for life.

The wise endure darkness, pressure, and loneliness so that greatness can be birthed. Fools quit at the first sign of darkness or pressure and are buried with their unrealized dreams.

2:13 The storehouse is built and ready to be filled, the tools have been sharpened, the sacks have been prepared, and the cart is set to haul loads to the market. The diligent farmer steps out of his hut, his bare feet in the soil. He looks down at his calloused hands, lifts his eyes up to his fields, and a smile spreads across his sun-beaten face. He has given all of himself. He has made every day an opportunity. Any day the fruit of his toil will come bursting through the ground into the light, and he is eager with expectation.

The wise leap from bed in the morning because they have cultivated a life that carries seeds of opportunity. They eagerly await the return on their investment—and any day can be the one that brings them breakthrough. Fools rise from bed in misery with no expectations from the day. There is nothing that can happen today that would change their life for the better, because they did not plant anything yesterday.

Those with eyes to see and ears to hear, let them see and hear!

Agisillus's dreams had been those of the farmer who plants his seed in uncultivated soil. He had accepted his dream and believed in it enough to sketch his tools and ideas, but he had planted in a mind which was still full of doubt, fear, and worry.

He had spent too much time thinking about what the others thought of him and taken their mockery to heart. He understood now he had planted his dream in a field of brush, clumps of earth, and rock. He never spent time figuring out logistics or costs of doing business. He never once asked for advice or even thought of finding someone whom he could learn from, and he had not buried this dream deep enough into the soil for it to take root. His dream was pecked at by the words of his peers and finally choked when disaster struck on the hot summer day he lost his mother and father.

He had read over the scroll several times, and when he finally looked up, the tavern was nearly full. The late-night crowd was thirsty. He felt a slight delay in his sight as his eyes scanned the room. His face felt hot like it always was when he drank. Now that he felt like he was a member of society; the busyness of the tavern made him cheerful instead of intimidated.

As a boy, he loved when his family would walk to the village banquets. They were his favorite summer evenings. The dances with all of the villagers were the most fun he ever had. As the bon fire roared, tone-deaf men bellowed their old songs of war. He always joined in, shouting the words at the top of his lungs with no regard for the sleeping forest creatures. He loved being around people—maybe this was why he put so much importance on what they thought of him and his dreams in the first place.

He waved at the barkeep for another beer. He would figure out how to cover the costs of supplies tomorrow— there was probably more than enough money in his pouch, and if not, he would just haggle with the merchants. He was drunk and no longer cared.

It was as if he had a second mind when he drank. A few beers gave him freedom from the endless analytical chatter of his mind. Life was easier when he didn't have to think so much.

***

The empty mugs nearly covered the barrel top. Agisillus put his lips against the edge of his current mug. He was deep in thought, watching the foam of the remaining beer swirl under the pressure of his breath. He leaned forward on his elbows, with arms crossed underneath his chest.

He wished now more than ever that his parents were alive. He would love to share with them all he was reading in the scrolls. Maybe he would even tell them that he would try to pursue his dream again, this time determined and armed with the ancient wisdom. If he would just become like the diligent farmer, he could succeed, too. His heart ached. He wanted his parents back; he wanted to be successful. But he had no idea where to start.

That was the thing about drinking. It had a way of relieving the pressure of life—making his troubles seem less significant and important, mysteriously keeping them at an emotional distance. But once he had too much, the troubles seemed to come back with a vengeance, and instead of thinking logically and reasonably, his emotions overwhelmed him. Suddenly his troubles were unbearable and out of control. Like a bad spirit, the memories always made their way back to him. They knew where to find their old friend.

When he was sober, a drink always seemed like a good idea, and no matter which way he analyzed it, he could never quite convince himself against one. The few months he'd spent working at The Watering Hole were the first time in years that he'd gone for so long without a drink—because he had kept himself busy. Now he was growing angry that once again he had been stupid enough to start drinking.

He remembered how impressed Vectimarius had been at his willingness to practice self-control.

Hah! What would Vectimarius say if he could see him now? He was just like the goat that continues to wrap its rope around the post, choking itself, no matter how many times its owner frees it.

Agisillus jumped when a burly man stumbled into his table and knocked several empty mugs to the floor.

The drunkard's bloodshot eyes drooped and took a few seconds to focus in on the skinny man sitting alone in the corner of the crowded tavern. He was sweating profusely, his long hair pulled back tight in a ponytail. He looked down at Agisillus's mug and the bony hand that was trying to steady it and ripped it from his grip. With one swig he emptied the contents and slammed it back on the table, foam still dripping from his tangled beard.

Agisillus's ears burned, and his heart began to pound in his chest. This wasn't the first time he'd faced another drunkard in a tavern, but he always managed to avoid a fight. Because he had no money to pay for drinks, he was practiced at staying out of the way. But this time he had paid and had every right to be in the tavern.

He quickly glanced over the man's massive shoulder, hoping the barkeep would intervene, but the man had not noticed the confrontation in the loud and crowded tavern. Through the lump in his throat he managed to croak out a few words. "I was not finished with my drink, sir," he said as he slowly stood up, tightly clutching the bag with the scrolls and money inside.

He'd watched plenty of tavern brawls. While there was never a good reason for one when drinking was involved, it was inevitable. With the Romans occupying the territory and the wars over, the warriors were now without purpose, and taverns were the place for them to do the only thing they were great at: drinking and brawling. He was thankful blades were now banned by the Romans. If a man were caught carrying one, it was assumed he was a part of the resistance, and the punishment could be death.

The mountain of a man laughed so hard it felt as if the floor shook. Then his face twisted into a scowl.

"It's time for you to go, Skinny," he growled. "This table is mine."

Agisillus clenched his hands together more tightly, hoping the man didn't notice them shaking, but just as he started moving to slide out from behind the keg, the man grabbed him by the neck and squeezed.

Agisillus swung his hands up and thrust them down to break the man's grip on his throat. He dipped his shoulder down and brought the entire weight of his body into his swing. The man's head towered nearly an elbow's length above his, but his fist found its hefty target. The fat cheek softened the blow to Agisillus's knuckles but he felt them connect to the jawbone, and the man's blood shot eyes rolled to the top of his head. He released a deep snore, the kind Agisillus had heard before when he saw a man knocked unconscious, and crumbled like a statue, crushing the neighboring table on the way down.

The entire tavern went silent and the wide-eyed audience stared at this most improbable scene. Agisillus turned and ran. He pushed all of his weight into the solid oak door and burst into the street. Suddenly a strong grasp tightened the collar of his tunic. His feet went flying from underneath him, and for a second he hung in the air horizontally before his body hit the cobblestone street with a thud.

Chapter 6
The Third Scroll: Resurrection

The clang of the iron bars rang in his ears as the door slammed behind him, echoing against the musty rock walls.

A few hours earlier, as he sprinted out of the tavern, a Roman patrol happened to be passing through the street. After they grabbed him, they pulled him from the ground and roughly tied his hands behind his back. He pleaded his case as the soldiers conversed with the barkeep. As far as the barkeep was concerned, the skinny vagabond was looking for trouble and had knocked his most loyal patron unconscious. The smell of beer on his breath and the baggy clothes didn't help. He was just another troublemaking lowlife.

He shifted around in the straw bedding, wishing that he had stayed in the room back at the inn instead of going to the tavern. The effects of the beer had worn off, and his head throbbed.

This was the way his life had gone these last few years. No matter how much he wanted to change, no matter how much he wanted to move forward and forget the past, no matter how much he promised himself he would start fresh, he ended up sabotaging any good thing that came his way.

He'd been so fortunate. The strange traveler had seen to his care, and Vectimarius had allowed him to stay long past the initial agreement. He had given him a job and trusted him with his money. And yet here he was, jailed just like another pathetic drunk. He could not argue with the Romans—what could he say? After all, he was a tramp, a drifter; he was nobody, no matter what lofty dreams he may have once had. Perhaps God was making him pay the price for all the times he had not been caught stealing beer.

He heard the soldier's leather sandals slapping on the stone floor, and the man appeared at the door, lifting a candelabrum high to peer into the cell. Agisillus held his breath in anticipation. Surely they would let him go now that he was sober.

"Tomorrow morning you're off to the fields," the guard said before turning and walking away.

His heart sank. He'd heard of the fields. Being sent to the fields made a man a public slave of Rome, and it happened to many Gauls. The slaves built roads, plowed fields, or repaired aqueducts, doing every backbreaking job imaginable until their sentence was served. He tried to reason with his fear. It wasn't the worst of punishments; violent criminals or enemies of Rome were often sent to the colosseums to be mauled by wild animals or simply used as target practice. It was great training for the gladiators and even better entertainment for blood-thirsty crowds. Things could be worse.

Agisillus sat in the mostly dark room and hugged his knees, pressing into his legs to protect himself from the chill that settled into the late hours. There would be no sleep for him tonight. Only a small window close to the ceiling let in a sliver of moonlight. How awful it was to know the barkeep would be expecting him any day now, yet he would not return. He would never be able to tell his side of the story. The man had relied on him but would now believe him to be a thief. He'd spent Vectimarius's money, lost his cart, and broken his trust.

***

The sky had just started to turn light when Agisillus finally drifted off. And it was only a few moments later that he was rudely awakened by the jailer slamming a club against the iron bars.

The man motioned for him to reach his arms through the bars and tied a rope around his wrists. As they stepped out into the street, he was shoved into the shoulder of another prisoner, and then they were tied together to a horse-drawn wagon.

Four soldiers accompanied the wagon. With a slap to the horse's coal-black hindquarters, the wagon lurched forward, and they marched down the street. Agisillus was thankful his hands were tied in front of him instead of behind him; he could pull his pants up around his waist whenever they started to sag. He hoped they wouldn't fall down with so many people watching as they paraded the criminals through town. His humiliation evaporated, however, when he saw people's reactions.

There was still much animosity toward Roman presence in the region, and he saw nods of approval rather than looks of reproach or disappointment for him and his silent companion. *The enemy of my enemy is my friend.* He remembered the ancient saying that certainly rang true here in Gorgiva.

Something had raised his spirits about an hour into the walk, and he finally took a deep inhale of the forest air, releasing the pressure of a night full of anxiety and worry. Several miles from the town, the wagon wheels lurched as the road changed from stone to dirt. In the back of the wagon his sack fell open from the jolt, and he saw the laced leather containing the scrolls. They were still with him!

A miracle! he thought.

Perhaps the soldiers would have the decency to let him keep his personal items, even though he was convinced he would never see what was left of the barkeep's money again.

The man tied next to him had noticed it too and with a guttural voice muttered without looking at him, "Is that bag yours?"

Agisillus was startled by the sudden question and looked back at the sack.

"Where did you get the scrolls?" the man asked before Agisillus could respond. Agisillus searched his mind for the shortest explanation for the most unusual of stories.

"A man I met left them for me as a gift," he said shyly, wondering why they piqued the man's curiosity.

"Was he strange looking—a giant man with furs over his shoulders?" the man asked.

Agisillus quickly nodded. "Have you met him!?" He hoped he would be able to tell him something more about the traveler.

When he looked at the man, he noticed the scar that came down the right side of his face, carving from his eye down to his jawbone. A dirty, bloody bandage wrapped his head.

"Yes, I met him. Came into a tavern I frequented and claimed to know me, but the fool talked too much and asked too many questions. He did not know how to mind his own affairs and accused me of wasting my life; he tried to give me that." He nodded at the scrolls.

"He said it would help me find purpose or something silly like that. I am sure it was one of those books the Druids read or some religious propaganda I don't care for." The man's raspy voice sounded like a stray dog growling over its food bowl and Agisillus listened carefully to catch every word. He dared not ask the man to repeat himself.

When he looked at Agisillus, the scar pulled his eyebrow and kept his eye nearly closed. "I put my blade to him and counted to three, and he was gone . . . him and his foolish 'secrets,' as he called them."

The man never spoke again, and Agisillus was glad he didn't.

He was obviously not interested in bettering his life. Agisillus wondered why the traveler had also approached this man. Perhaps he wanted to help the man turn things around as well? Was he like this ragged thief? Whatever the reason, he was grateful the traveler gifted the scrolls to him instead.

The scrolls gave him a renewed sense of purpose. As if he had a hidden treasure no one could know about, a secret that could help him turn his miserable life around. The words never left him. When he read them, not through the eyes of his past but simply to comprehend, out of duty to the traveler who had gifted them, he began to accept them as a prescription for better living, a way to stop hating himself and his life. When seen as warnings rather than condemnation, the proverbs became agreeable.

They made him feel something he hadn't felt in a long time. It was hope, a feeling he was once familiar with, long ago. It was that same powerful energy and excitement he felt as a boy when he first believed he could do something great with his life.

As skeptical as he first had been while reading through the proverbs of the diligent farmer, the words of the scrolls resonated with him, and he felt as if they somehow sank deeper, past his analytical mind. Truth seeps through the toughest of egos. Truth does not tiptoe around those easily offended. Truth, once it's brought to the light, cannot be dismissed. He understood that now.

He held his arms out in front of him to keep the stiff rope from rubbing his wrists raw and wished he could climb onto the back of the wagon. His sore feet needed a break. As they walked, he stole glances at the man tied to him but was careful to avoid eye contact. He looked to be quite accustomed to this type of treatment, as if it were almost routine for him. Perhaps he was one of the many rebels still trying to lead a revolt against the Romans.

As far as Agisillus could see, the Romans provided opportunity. When he was a boy, however, he hated the Romans because everybody else did. He often eavesdropped on the gossip of worried adults in the village and built resentment toward these unwelcomed oppressors before he ever laid eyes on one. Thanks to the scrolls, he was realizing that what stood in between him and his dream was the limited thinking of his fellow villagers, not the excuses they'd convinced him to accept or the fears they spread about Romans. Romans were industrious and innovative, and this was why they were the superior nation. Their ever-expanding empire required more resources by the day. He saw that the Gauls who were willing to provide those resources gained wealth quickly.

Now he understood that if he had found a blacksmith years ago willing to work with him on credit and create the tools he had drawn, the power-drunk Romans could have been his ideal customers. He swore to himself he would become the diligent farmer; he would never let opportunity out of his sight again. He hoped somehow he would get the scrolls back; he needed them now more than ever.

Beneath his feet, the beaten clay and solid troughs cut by wagon wheels suggested this was a heavily traveled route. Many smaller roads forked in various directions, each presumably leading to another town or village. Agisillus tried to read the signposts pointing in one direction or another but could not recognize any names. He had never been this far from home.

The massive Corsican pine trees on each side formed a tunnellike passage, providing shade from the sun and a cool dampness in the air. The sunrays found their way through small openings in the branches, sending golden beams through the fog. Moss carpeted the forest floor with billions of tiny blades and laid out a flawless layer of green between the thick tree trunks.

For a moment, Agisillus marveled at the beauty—until his mind snapped back to the uncertainty that lay ahead, and the usual anxiety returned.

He started crafting a plan: if he kept his head down and worked as hard as he could for the duration of his sentence without causing any more trouble, surely he would be released. And wouldn't his crime be trivial when compared with other prisoners?

He caught one of the signs that said "Rome" and hoped they were not going that far. He knew what that could mean. The crop fields extended far into the countryside near the city, and due to demand, new wheat fields were being plowed and planted every day. There were rumors that many of those who were captured and forced to work in the fields never returned—although he had never personally known anyone who'd disappeared.

The longer they walked, the more Roman scouts they encountered on the road. The soldiers always stopped to greet each other with a loud "*Ave!*" and a salute, followed by a few minutes of banter, their voices echoing high into the treetops.

They walked in and out of one heavily wooded area after another as the road wove through hills and forests. Every now and then they would enter a clearing from which he spotted the sea far away in the distance.

When night came, they stretched out on the mossy floor and the soldiers lit a fire, then changed shifts every few hours to stand guard. Agisillus never slept for more than a few minutes, constantly awoken by the crackling of the fire or because the man he was tied to shifted to get more comfortable. Even the slightest tug on the ropes burned his wrists.

He stared up at the stars barely peeking through the branches of the towering trees and softly prayed. He prayed like he saw his father do, moving his lips but keeping his words inaudible.

His father often mocked the Druids in the village with their potions, oils, dances, and chants. *"They dance themselves silly and are amused at their own hallucinations, thinking they heard the spirits,"* he had laughed. *"But God only speaks to a humbled heart."*

The students were taught by Druids at school, and his father hated that they would also teach religion. *"There is but one God,"* he would always remind Agisillus.

Agisillus prayed that if there was a God who watched over him and all of creation, he would protect him from whatever was to happen in the days to come, like he had once protected his father at war.

He begged God's forgiveness for wasting his life and for living like the fools in the parables from the scrolls. He prayed to be like the diligent farmer.

If he were lucky enough to ever be free again, he promised God he would fight for his dreams and plant his seed—even though at this moment he was further from his dreams than he had ever been.

And he prayed Vectimarius could forgive him for not returning. Then he fell asleep recounting his conversation with the strange traveler on that night that was going to be his last.

***

"He's a reader, Lucius." The soldier laughed and yanked on the rope. "Maybe you keep this one in the palace—

he's too skinny for the fields."

Two carved wooden doors had swung open, and a well-groomed man stepped out into the courtyard and walked toward the group. His tunic was sewn with a gold trim around the sleeves and waistline, and it flowed behind him like silk. The dark leather sandals strapped nearly up to his knees were polished and oiled and creaked with every confident step. The man adjusted the belt around his waist, revealing strong shoulders and muscular arms that flexed with every slight movement. He nodded at the two soldiers standing guard near the ivy-wrapped columns supporting the second story balcony just above the door.

A servant girl was pouring water from a vase into the flowerpots that lined the railing, curiously peeking at the new arrivals. The prison crew had finally come to a stop in the courtyard after walking up the mountain road to what Agisillus assumed was this man's tremendous home. He'd never seen anything like it; the estate could have been a village of its own.

A full statue of a naked man with only a sword at his waist stood in the middle of the courtyard, surrounded by a garden of red and white roses. Rows of cypress trees lined the wide stone-paved road that led up to the palace. The thin trees had quivered in the breeze as the slow-moving group passed by.

Agisillus could see past the clay slats of the palace roof to the hills behind the building and the fields which covered nearly the entire side of the mountain. Smaller clay huts separated what looked to be an olive grove from a wheat field, and he saw slaves hoeing a roped-off area, perhaps preparing it for expansion. Several lightly-armored soldiers paced in the dirt in between the slaves; others chatted in the shade of the huts.

The Roman man's beard was neatly trimmed along his jawline. His eyes were outlined with a dark charcoal, something Agisillus had only ever seen on the prostitutes who hung around taverns in big towns. A sheen of oil made his curly black hair glisten in the sun. Agisillus later learned the man was named Lucius and he was the minister of agriculture of the Roman Empire.

The man briefly glanced at Agisillus but then fixed his eyes on the prisoner tied to him as if recognizing him.

"You simply cannot accept the new way of the world, can you?" he said, still staring at the prisoner who kept his head down and never looked up to meet Lucius's glare. "Straight to the fields with him," he ordered a nearby soldier. "Assign him to a hut with the others but no bedding for him until he learns to appreciate the mercy bestowed upon him."

The man must have been an escapee, Agisillus guessed, and he was relieved to see Lucius was reasonable. An escaped slave would often be executed, but judging by the bandage around his head, this one only took a beating when captured. One of the soldiers who accompanied the group untied the ropes and walked the prisoner down a path that led behind the estate.

Lucius turned his attention to Agisillus and examined the new arrival. Agisillus straightened his back. "Sir, I have not committed any crimes," he said as he pulled up his loose trousers with his bound hands. "I was keeping to myself, a paying customer at the tavern, and a man attacked me." The soldiers laughed, and the man raised his hand to silence them.

"I'm not one you plead your case with—I simply take who they send me," he responded. Lucius turned to the soldiers. "What is his sentence?" he asked.

"The officer gave him a month of hard labor," one of them responded. "But you can keep him as long as you would like, sir. Looks to be an aimless fellow—perhaps working in the fields will teach him a thing or two about how the world turns."

Agisillus shifted nervously, waiting for the response. A month of labor seemed an extreme punishment, especially since the other man had started the fight, but this was the first time he'd learned what his sentence was, and he felt slightly relieved. The stories he had heard of men being captured by the Romans and never seen again had frightened and worried him throughout the journey.

I could survive a month of labor, he thought as he stood there. After all, hard work was nothing new to him. *I could serve my sentence, make it back to The Watering Hole, apologize to Vectimarius, and start earning money to repay him.*

"So you can read . . . but you likely can't write, can you?" Lucius asked. "Yes sir," Agisillus replied, stealing a glance at the scrolls in the back of the cart. Lucius followed his glance and reached into the cart for the leather wrap containing the scrolls. Agisillus anxiously pulled up his pants as the man loosened the string and unrolled the scrolls.

Lucius studied the first few lines on the fragile sheets. His eyebrows shot up.

"Wise reading for a mere vagabond," he nodded as he kept reading. "Where did you get this? This is text I would expect to find among the libraries of philosophers and learned men, not in the hands of a"—he paused and looked Agisillus up and down before he finished his sentence— "a Gaul."

"It was gifted to me, sir," Agisillus stammered, a lump forming in his throat.

Would the man even believe him? What if he was accused of stealing them? The blood rushed to his face, and he tried to calm himself, straightening his shoulders. The scrolls were his only valuable possession in this world. If he lost them, he would truly have nothing. They were his little window of hope, and if he could just study them, become like that farmer, he could turn his life around. He could live better. Tears burned his eyes, and he quickly looked down to hide them. Lucius noticed. The man slowly rolled the leather, tied up the strings, and pressed the scrolls into Agisillus's chest.

"Keep them," he said with a nod of approval.

Agisillus nodded and clutched his treasure with both hands.

"Take him inside, give him a change of clothes, and assign him to the groundskeepers. We've got enough bodies in the fields," Lucius instructed the assistant who had walked up during the conversation.

Agisillus followed the boy through a gate and down a path that ran along a stone wall. As they walked to the back of the estate, he saw other slaves in the distance, their backs burned from days in the sun, hacking at the rocky dirt on the mountainside. Others swung scythes in the wheat fields, and the sound of the blades slicing through the yellow sea of kernels carried over the distance.

The sound reminded him how happy it made him when his father let him swing the scythe as a boy, even though he damaged more crops than he harvested.

To his surprise, they turned and walked through another gate and entered into the property, away from the slave huts he had noticed earlier. He had assumed that is where he would stay. A large pool stretched toward the palace, bordered by wide marble tiles, and leading up the steps toward the palace patio were more statues of figures of what appeared to be gods and goddesses. Agisillus wondered how the artists chiseled the stones so smooth.

Water flowed from a turning waterwheel into the grand pool, which was surrounded by more of the beautiful cypress trees. A flower garden bursting with roses was tended by tunic-bearing slaves. Agisillus soaked in the serenity and peacefulness of the magical scene.

This is wealth worth working for. This is the reward of the diligent farmer! He inhaled deeply, as if he could absorb this place. He remembered the proverb, *The diligent farmer walks past the harvest of others, and when his eyes see their success, he becomes inspired all the more.*

At the rear of the estate, a smaller complex connected the palace walls. Its rooftop matched the red clay slats atop the palace. As they pushed through the creaking oak door, they stepped into a shaded patio area that opened up to a courtyard and a garden with a shallow circular pond in the center. The pond was neatly outlined by smooth river stones, more rosebushes, and narrow pathways that snaked through the garden.

The servant, still not saying a word, walked Agisillus to a doorway facing the garden and stopped in front of it. Brushing the navy-blue curtain aside, the servant unlatched a steel bar which barricaded the solid door and elbowed it open. Agisillus realized the curtain served to hide the barricaded room, perhaps to make the servants' housing area look less like a jail.

Agisillus stepped through a narrow hallway lined with ghostly faces engraved into the tile. He found the partial statues ugly; he didn't understand the Roman fascination with the charcoaled eyes and oiled curls. Even the statues of men looked feminine.

Inside, the room was large but cozy: carpets hung down each wall, and a red wool blanket covered the bed. Surely this wasn't a slave's room. This was luxury compared to the huts near the fields, just a few hundred meters away. If this were to be his room for a month, he would be pleasantly surprised. It would be the best sleeping quarters he had ever slept in.

"You will stay here for now," the servant said. "Every day at dusk, return the tools to the shed and come here. Someone will come by and make sure you are in your cell, leave food, and lock the door for the night." He kicked at a wood bucket. "Use this if you need to relieve yourself, and empty it in the back near the wall in the morning when your room is unlocked."

Agisillus looked at the bucket, an upgrade compared to his typical bathroom. Exposing his bare rear-end in the woods, sometimes in the snow, was just about the worst part of his experience as a vagabond over these last few years. One miserable night when he was trying to relieve himself while drunk, he lost balance while squatting and toppled over, landing on his own feces. The next day he shivered knee-deep in the creek as he washed his trousers in the icy water.

"I will come for you before the rooster crows," the servant said and tossed a clump of white clothing onto the cot. "Bathe in the basin out back, and put on this tunic." He closed the heavy door, and Agisillus heard the steel bar slide into place behind him.

The torches on the wall had not been lit, but the setting sun illuminated the room through the air vents near the ceiling. He laid the tunic out on the bed and stared at it. He would look like a Roman in it, but at least it was clean. His own stained clothes had grown loose, and he was tired of pulling up his trousers.

He plopped onto the cot, grateful to have the scrolls, and began to carefully unlace the leather strings.

Scroll 3 The Resurrection

3:1 The diligent farmer runs to his fields and crouches with his face to the dirt, where rows and rows of fragile green shoots have come peeking through. He lies on his back beside them, wipes his tears, looks to the sky, and says, "Thank you."

Like all men, the wise are anxious, eager, even impatient, and yet they continue to believe that what they toil over will one day come to pass. Fools are also anxious, eager, impatient, but soon they stop believing. They experience a life of frustration, bitterness, resentment, and regret.

3:2 The diligent farmer attends a gathering of elders. Other farmers, wise in their years and experience, advise the young farmers of all they must do in order to reap a good harvest and find success in their toils. Ten men hear the message, but by the time the candle has faded, only one—the diligent farmer—remains at the table.

Ten men hear a good message.

Nine will be inspired.

Eight will be inspired a short time later.

Seven will take notes to look back on later.

Six will talk of all they will accomplish.

Five will hope it's possible for them.

Four will believe it's possible for them.

Three will take action.

Two will fight through some of the fears and obstacles that appear along the way.

One, only one, will persist long enough to succeed.

The wise are the one who persists. Fools are the nine who fall away somewhere along the way.

3:3 The diligent farmer tiptoes in his fields around rows of plants peeking through the dirt and prudently tends them. He is mindful not to misplace his tools, careful not to step where he might damage the plants, and watchful that the wild creatures stay far from the tender shoots.

The wise are diligent in their care for their dreams knowing desperation kills momentum. Fools see some progress and leave their jobs, brag to the naysayers, and accrue debt because they believe they will be rich, but they will soon know only poverty.

3:4 The diligent farmer does not make unnecessary commitments. He does away with petty distractions. For a time, he does not play and only increases his labor. He is nearing a successful harvest, and it is now more than ever that his fields need his attention and the care of his calloused hands.

The wise become obsessed all the more when they are close to realizing their dream. They understand that those who give all of themselves to their dream and cut away all distractions will do great things. Fools have selfish intentions; they crave recognition and a life of ease, and once they have a small taste of success, they celebrate in excess with their friends.

3:5 The diligent farmer cannot reap his harvest alone; the work is too great for one man. He does not purchase unnecessary things and saves money to hire more help and prepare for the big harvest. He knows the time is now or never.

The wise know true success requires investing much money and time. They temporarily sacrifice comfort and pleasure for a greater reward. For them, it is an easy decision to make. Fools have not been faithful with little and therefore cannot be faithful with much. They cannot trust themselves to make large investments. They are ruled by lack and never achieve great things.

3:6   The diligent farmer is never fully satisfied with his harvest. Year after year, he continues to tend to the plants and tries new fertilizer. He is always trimming, pruning, and looking for ways to grow better crops.
The wise are never satisfied with their final product or service; they continue to master their craft, perfect their product, and refine their service. Fools work for the reward and can't be bothered with excellence. Soon they are overtaken and outsold by those who provide better service to mankind.

3:7   The diligent farmer does not eat at the village banquet if he did not contribute harvest from his fields. He never expects something for nothing. He does not extend his hand for charity from his wealthy friends. People see him toil day after day in the fields, but he does not complain, and because of this, they are willing to help him all the more.
The wise do not look upon the purse of another and demand distribution of wealth. Fools expect something for nothing; they feast upon the labor of others and lay down still hungry in the grave of poverty.

3:8   The diligent farmer is eager to expand his business. He purchases more land and prepares for more crops than he is yet able to maintain, but he knows it is only in this way he will have a harvest like the wealthy and successful farmers.
The wise seek to be in environments they do not yet belong in. Tomorrow they are to be in a room of important men, so today they lay awake anxious at night, losing sleep. In the morning they show up despite their fears. They understand they can only grow when they are stretched and uncomfortable. Fools make sure to schedule no such appointments. They are soon surpassed by the wise as they lie fast asleep in their cozy beds.

3:9 The diligent farmer prays over his fields every day and continues to give thanks. It is his hands that are calloused, it is his feet that are sore, it is his back that is breaking, but even though he bleeds from his hands and sweat runs down his cheeks, he always remembers the magic of the seed and his covenant with the Creator. He shares with Him in the joy as he eagerly awaits sure success.

The wise do not lose sight of what they possess. They understand their work, their success, their failures, their troubles, and their victories are all a gift which is here today but may be gone tomorrow. Fools puff their chest with pride in their successes but blame the heavens for their failures and soon will lose everything.

3:10 The diligent farmer wakes in the night to hear the sound of hail beating the ground and crushing his crops. He rises early the very next day and heads to the fields. He rakes the soil, props up the seedlings, and prays the broken plants will survive.

The wise understand storms come upon all—on the evil and on the good, on the foolish and on the wise—and do not curse the skies when trouble arises. Fools scream at the heavens in which they had no faith in to begin with and become faithless all the more. They never prosper, because blame is a disease that destroys prosperity.

3:11 The diligent farmer has withstood the storms, the droughts, the floods, and the animals that have threatened his fields. He stands among a small group of successful farmers at the market and is envied by the lazy farmers whose inactivity is now exposed.

The wise are like wheat on the threshing floor: they withstand the pressure and the winnowing. Fools are the chaff that is separated and thrown away.

3:12 The diligent farmer has been faithful in his work. He has persisted. He has grown his empire and become one with his dream. He has stretched himself beyond previous limitations. He has been faithful in his steps as he walked with enthusiasm and hope. He has not blamed, he has given thanks, and he is full of joy. He enjoys the bountiful fruits of his labor.

Those with eyes to see and ears to hear, let them see and hear!

Chapter 7
The Fourth Scroll: Harvest

Agisillus jerked awake to the clanking of the barred door. He jumped to his feet and quickly slipped the tunic left for him over his head. It was still dark out, but through the open courtyard he could see the stars had faded and the sky was starting to brighten.

He had read the scroll marked "3" several times until he had fallen asleep. Something about the proverb of the diligent farmer propping up his plants beaten by the storm kept his mind running throughout the night. He could not remember if he had dreamt it or simply pictured it vividly.

How faithful could one possibly be to not curse the heavens when such disaster struck in life? He thought about his own misery and how quickly he had been filled with hatred and anger. He wanted that kind of faith—to be filled with belief and be so strong willed that he couldn't be swayed when trouble came. *"They never prosper, because blame is a disease that destroys prosperity."*

It was true. He had done it all his life. When life was unfolding favorably for him, he boasted about all he had done, but when favor and luck ran out, he was quick to shake an angry fist at the heavens, to which he had given no glory when all was well.

A servant entered the room accompanied by a guard. At the estate, the guards were not armed like typical Roman soldiers. They carried only a sword sheathed at their waist—perhaps the standard uniform rules were relaxed for the slave overseers. Agisillus glanced down at his tunic and noticed that now he looked nearly identical to these two men. He followed them out of the courtyard and to the back shed where several others had already gathered.

The servant pointed to the garden and handed him a garden pick. All day he hacked at the weeds as fast as he could, hoping to impress the servant, who watched him from a distance. The sun was high above his head as he bent over the garden near the pool, raking his hands through the dirt around the rose bushes and lavender surrounding him. He did not mind tending to flowers and playing in the dirt, and would have even enjoyed himself if not for the circumstance.

He kept at it. Perhaps he should have worked this hard when he was free. He had been lucky to be assigned to this job, but any day the circumstances could change again, and he feared the rough treatment of the men in the fields, hoping he would not find himself there. He knew he was at the mercy of Lucius.

Late that afternoon, Lucius emerged from the palace with several scrolls tucked under his arm and briskly walked to a marble table near the pool where he dropped the scrolls and sat down. Agisillus was kneeling in a garden bed just a few yards away and could see the minister's eyebrows scrunched and forehead wrinkled into a frown. He guessed Lucius was bothered by something. The servant quickly grabbed him by the arm and started to tug on him to move away but Lucius waved his arm and said, "Please continue working." The servant released his grip on his arm.

Agisillus had his back to the other slaves and had not noticed them scatter when Lucius came near. Now, with permission from Lucius, the others returned to their spots and got busy tending to the garden. He would need to be much more observant and learn the rules quickly. Nobody had warned him, but judging by their reactions, he realized he should have left the garden as well the moment the minister arrived.

A fat man led by two servants joined Lucius at the table. He was outfitted in a soldier's uniform with a scarlet tunic and leather vest and sandals laced up to his knees, but he was unarmed. *Perhaps a high-ranking official*, Agisillus thought. *With his heavy breathing and sloppy uniform with the dark sweat stains under his arms, he certainly doesn't resemble an officer, though.*

Their conversation carried to where Agisillus was spreading handfuls of manure underneath each bush.

When he heard Lucius say, "This could be disastrous," he crawled to a bed of flowers closer to where the two sat. "The more we grow the sloppier things get," Lucius continued. "The amount of grain we bring in per acre in these cursed hills is a fraction to what we gather in Rome. You simply can't match the work of capable farmers with the production from forced labor."

The fat soldier had taken off his helmet and set it on his knee, wiping his forehead with his arm. "We can whip them near to death, but you can't teach these barbarians how to properly farm. They're fighters, animals, and reproduce like rabbits—that they do well—but crack a whip on their backs and they start poking and prodding at the dirt as if it is a foreign object," he said. His voice was throaty and froglike. His face grew red as he spoke, and his double chin cushioned his fast-moving jaw.

Agisillus could not tell if the man was red with frustration or if the heat from his body, being trapped by the leather vest strapped tightly around his chest, was slowly cooking him. His belly strained against the leather until the vest looked as if it would burst.

"I'm looking forward to the day we wipe them off the face of the earth once and for all, but until we do that, we'll have to use them any way we can," he said, sponging his sweating brow with a cloth.

Lucius sat in silence, immersed in thought. After a minute he leaned forward, placing his elbows on his thighs and his hands under his chin.

"Listen. We could clear all the land from Rome to the ends of the earth to plow fields and still never produce enough to survive this famine if we don't figure out a way to get the most from all we've already done. The pressure from Rome is only rising; they say it could be the worst harvest we've seen in generations. We use slaves because we don't have enough farmers to sustain all of the land. But these slaves do more damage to the fields than good—and why shouldn't they? They are enslaved—to them it would be better if we starved and crumbled. They have nothing to lose. I cannot find blame in that—I might do the same if I were in their shoes."

Agisillus crawled to a rose bush that he'd already trimmed but which was closer to the conversation. The Romans were afraid of a coming famine? How could the most powerful empire in all of the land have a shortage of food? If the Romans were in trouble, with all of their resources, how would the Gauls fare in a famine? Surely the Romans would come from far and wide and simply take what they needed from every village, town, and family. They were the superior force.

The Gallic wars had already destroyed so many lives and settlements, what would a famine look like? Famine would mean death to all the people who stood in the way of Romans; they had already proved they would stop at nothing. The Romans would take everything. What success could he have, what wealth could he gain if there was nothing left?

A wave of guilt washed over him and echoed in his empty belly, as he thought of his parents and what they would do in this situation. His father would have gladly died to defend his people and his family. His mother would give her last morsel to feed starving countrymen. And here he was, so preoccupied with his own misery and loathing all these years, so obsessed with blaming the people back in his village that he never once thought about how noble his family had actually been—and how far he had truly fallen from his roots.

But he could do differently now.

He needed to get to the fields. He knew how to farm, and he could help the other slaves do their work. Perhaps he could help slow the spreading famine.

He stood up and walked toward the servant who had been watching over him.

***

"You have been assigned to the gardens," the servant replied.

"I can farm. I grew up on a farm," Agisillus pleaded. "I have helped my mother and father since I was a boy. I can help you produce better crops more quickly!"

"Lucius is the minister of agriculture of the Roman Empire—are you suggesting he has not already exhausted every resource? Do you accuse him of being ignorant? Proper farming is not the problem—it's that you lazy Gauls can't be whipped hard enough to dig, plant, and harvest properly!"

Agisillus stepped back in shock. He hadn't expected such a violent response.

"You either dig the furrows too deep and the seeds never grow or you dig shallow furrows and the seed never survives the elements. And the more overseers they bring in, the more resistance there is. There are not enough eyes to watch and make sure you dirty slaves do the work properly."

"The famine is coming—and a skinny, pathetic man like you will do more damage than good out there. I suggest you be thankful you were selected to be here, because they will break you out there. You will not survive a day in the fields. Get back to your garden." The servant sneered and snapped his fingers at Agisillus—waving him away.

Agisillus's ears burned. He turned back and headed for the garden. Every part of him wanted to slug the nervy servant, but if he did, he would surely be killed. His fiery reaction is what got him here in the first place. He couldn't keep his hands from shaking with rage.

He was likely the only prisoner who had a skillful hand in digging the furrows properly; he had done so all his youth. The others were warriors, criminals, rebels; of course they would destroy any field they plowed with their clumsy hands and feet, especially when they were laboring against their will.

"There's no plentiful harvest if there is no love in a farmer's heart," his mother had always said when the young Agisillus would complain about his chores.

His thoughts raced as he plucked dead rose petals. Even if he could gather the courage to convince Lucius to let him work in the fields, he was only one man. He could not make a difference.

And then it hit him. He stopped trimming the roses and froze with his knees and knuckles in the dirt, staring down at the ground. The sketches he used to draw, the ideas he had to build farming tools, all the ideas he never followed through on. They could help prevent this crisis—he knew they could! The servant had mentioned how the slaves weren't digging proper furrows. The sketches he'd drawn were the design for a furrow digger!

He'd first gotten the idea when he had tried to help his mother and father plow their fields with more ease. They could never grow quite enough of one crop to sell the extra at the market. The tool would have helped them manage much larger fields and instead of growing small amounts of different crops, they could grow a lot of a single one like wheat and make a profit on the extra.

He imagined a tool that could be pulled behind an ox or a bull, or even an ass, that would allow a farmer to dig acres of furrows in a matter of hours—each furrow just the proper depth for planting wheat. The same work would take a man several days. It had been one of the tools he had wanted to build when he worked in the blacksmith shop.

Tears welled up in his eyes. It all made sense now. He understood why he was here, a few feet from the minister of agriculture—the only person in the entire world who needed the very thing he had once dreamed of creating. Being here was no accident at all.

He thought of that tavern so far away. Something else had occurred that fateful evening. The strange traveler was no ordinary man, and it was as if his very spirit had been guiding Agisillus ever since. And the caravan when he was nine, the scrolls, the diligent farmer, and the gift of dreams from the Creator the man had spoken of . . . all were connected, and all had prepared him for this very moment. The ideas the man had planted into his mind had finally begun to sprout.

He wiped his eyes, smearing his bony cheeks with soil and tears. The fat soldier had left, and Lucius was sitting alone reading a scroll. Agisillus hesitated, glanced to make sure the servant wasn't looking, and began to walk toward the minister. As he approached the seated Lucius, who had not yet noticed him, a shout startled him and the minister both.

The servant leapt over a row of bushes with an armed soldier not far behind. Agisillus froze. Before he could explain himself, the servant reached him and with a closed fist struck Agisillus hard in the side of the head. Then, grabbing a fistful of his hair, the servant yanked him flat on his back.

Lucius jumped from his seat and stood in shock. Because of the servant's reaction and the garden pick in Agisillus's hand, everyone assumed he intended harm. The servant and soldier grabbed under his elbows, their fingers digging into his flesh as they hauled him up from the ground. Breathing hard, the servant began to apologize to Lucius, but Agisillus shouted over him:

"Sir, I meant no harm! I need to talk to you about the fields!" They would surely kill him—it was now or never. "Sir, I had an idea for your fields . . . Sir, please—an idea for your fields!"

Lucius's face relaxed as he took a deep breath in and then exhaled. "Give him a moment to speak," he said to the two men, his eyes fixed on Agisillus.

The servant began to argue but Lucius snapped, "Enough!" and the man went silent, still tightly gripping Agisillus's arm.

"Sir, I was a farmer all my youth, my mother and father taught me everything there is to know about farming, and, sir, I have an idea that can help you with the fields." Agisillus's voice shook as the words spilled out in a torrent. Any second now they would pull him away.

"Sir, my mother and father died working in the field . . ." His voice choked, and he fought hard not to cry in front of the man.

"And I have an idea to help you make the furrows."

"I believe it will help you . . . It really can. I know the prisoners are hurting the fields more than they are helping; there's a way to till the fields much faster and more efficiently than a man with a hoe!"

Lucius ran his fingers through his hair. He held his hands on his hips for a moment, looking at his pile of scrolls and then back at Agisillus. He motioned to the chair in front of him, and again the servant began to protest. This time no words had to be spoken—the glare Lucius shot his way was enough, and the two yanked Agisillus down to sit on the chair.

The soldier held on to his fistful of Agisillus's tunic. A few more curious soldiers had stepped out of the palace onto the tile patio, and servant girls peeked over the stone balcony railing to witness the commotion.

What a sight it must have been—a scrawny Gaul seated at the table across from the powerful minister of agriculture. Lucius dropped a handful of scrolls to the patio next to him and kept one scroll on the marble table. He slid the open scroll toward Agisillus and placed a clay ink jar and a metal pen next to it.

"Show me."

Agisillus picked up the pen, hands still shaking, and dipped the point in the jar.

"Sir, I overheard you talking about the prisoners not digging the land properly . . ." He paused and swallowed hard, trying to moisten his throat that was suddenly dry.

"I know that some furrows are too shallow, some too deep, producing a weak crop. But if you were to cast an iron plow shaped like a spear at the tip and add plates to the sides to consistently keep the plow flat on the soil, there would always be an even furrow and all of the hard work would be left to the animal pulling it."

Agisillus began to lightly sketch the device he had envisioned so many times, dipping the pen into the ink jar as he spoke.

"What one man could do in a day with the right tool and a pair of oxen, the slaves couldn't do in a week, sir." He cleared his throat; the shakiness in his words gone. His eyes widened, and he leaned closer to Lucius, who had one arm across his chest, hand tucked under his armpit and the other supporting his chin.

Agisillus continued describing the very tool he was once mocked for conceiving. Here he was seated across an important man, a Roman, and yet the man was hearing him out, sparing a moment to listen. Something the people of his village never did.

A slight smile formed on the pursed lips of the minister, and the wrinkles around his eyes deepened as he watched the young, skinny Gaul speak with enthusiasm and passion. Ink was dripping over the marble as the young man's bony hand went back and forth from the jar to the paper, moving sloppily at first and then slowing masterfully as he sketched. Agisillus would stop, cock his head to look over his sketch, and then continue scribbling as he drew the device, the fields, and even a fat ox strapped to the end of it with a rope.

The minister turned to look at the fat soldier who had come back to investigate the ruckus and raised his eyebrows.

"Looks like the gods are showing us a little mercy," he said, and then turned his head back to the sketch. Agisillus had finished, and Lucius raised it with a wave through the air to let the ink dry.

The fat soldier impatiently wiped his forehead with his hairy arm—the scowl never left his face. He glanced for a moment at the sketch and then glared at Agisillus, who was now standing behind Lucius. He must have been informed of what had taken place after he left, and he was visibly furious. Agisillus kept his eyes down at the table, not daring to meet the man's glare.

"How about we throw this wheat-thin chap into the fields for a day or two, and we'll see just how many ideas he comes up with then," the man growled. "This barbarian is going to teach us to farm? I have an overseer in the fields who knows just how to deal with the 'clever' ones . . . I'm sure he has room for one more in his crew of mutts."

Lucius whipped his head around and locked eyes with the

obese soldier. "You, my friend, appear to be a large part of our problem," he snapped, sticking his finger straight into the man's protruding belly.

"I see in my reports that the fields to the west of Mount Viso, the ones you were tasked to oversee, have been among the worst, hardly producing any wheat. It is exactly why I ordered you here today in the first place, and you could not explain yourself. If you don't have a solution to offer, I recommend you keep that loose tongue of yours from flapping—or join the slaves in the field."

Lucius stood quickly, rolled the sketch, and picked up the other scrolls from the tile.

"Put him back to work in the garden," he told the servant as he pointed at Agisillus. "But tomorrow morning, make sure he's ready to join me at sunrise. Prepare my wagon and inform the other estates I will be inspecting every acre of land from here to Gallia Celtica. We've got no time to spare fiddling our thumbs and resting our asses. This could help our efforts, and sure as the gods are watching over us, I will find out. I must answer to the emperor himself next month, and I'll be damned if I don't have a solution for him."

Agisillus's stomach turned. He had only heard the words *Gallia Celtica*, once. When the Gallic Wars, as they were now called, had ended, the Romans divided the regions and renamed them. His village was located in what the Romans had claimed as Gallia Celtica!

He could not show his face there again. But, he reasoned, the region was massive; he had heard of Roman estates and slave fields but had never seen one anywhere near his village. The chances of them coming close to the place he had been drinking to forget were very unlikely.

His fingernails dug deep into the dirt, and he yanked weeds from around the roses even faster than he had before. His mind was racing. He was nearly bursting with excitement that Lucius had affirmed his idea. If he overheard the servants correctly, Lucius was planning to take the sketch to a blacksmith in the next town. The estate and most of the Roman farmlands had extended so far that they were closer to the Gauls than to Rome. Gauls would be the ones hammering and shaping his invention! The idea danced in his mind over and over, and his entire body buzzed with excitement.

***

The next day dawned strangely warm. The stars still glimmered as Agisillus followed a servant through the estate. Instead of walking around the back wall to the front courtyard, they walked near the pool where he had desperately pitched his invention idea to the minister just hours before and headed for the back entrance of the palace. The slap of his leather sandals on the tile and the light breeze blowing the torches along the way were the only sound in the dark as they walked in silence.

Large silk curtains covered the open entrance to the palace and flowed like a burgundy waterfall in the breeze. As they walked up the patio steps, Agisillus could see the spacious corridor through them, illuminated brightly by more massive torches. The opening stretched the entirety of the building, leading all the way to a hallway near the front.

They brushed the curtains aside and stepped into the palace. The arched ceiling soared above them, and the second story hallways to either side of them were bordered by a marble railing. Thick pillars of polished marble propped up the upper floor and from each hung a golden bowl that held an oil torch, the flames dancing and reflecting brightly off the metal. On each side of the open hallway on the upper floor, dark-stained double doors faced each other across the atrium. Agisillus wondered how many people lived in the palace. One would have quite a walk just to get from one room to the next.

At the far end of the corridor, two flights of stairs with hand-carved railings wound down from either side of the second floor and met at the entrance. An armed soldier stood near the curtains covering the door and flung them open as they approached. He nodded at the servant but looked surprised to see Agisillus, who tried hard to keep his eyes from visibly wandering and soaking in the beauty of the grand hall.

He must have been a sight to behold. The servant had awakened him an hour before and stood watch as Agisillus bathed in a basin in the courtyard. Instead of wearing the same tunic, the servant had handed him a fresh one lined with gold thread around the sleeves and a pair of sandals, never worn. He had struggled with them, and the servant had to help strap them all the way up to the middle of his shins. He blushed when the servant applied the charcoal around his eyes and spread oil into his hair.

Long hallways lined with statues extended to either side of the palace. At the end of the hallway to his right, an entire wall of shelving from floor to ceiling held hundreds of scrolls. He had never seen an actual library. *That must be where the strength of the Roman Empire lies*, he thought. *While we Gauls build massive storehouses for beer, Romans build such libraries.*

As they stepped into the courtyard, the same courtyard in which he'd stood terrified only a few days before, a covered wagon pulled by two raven-black horses rolled up in front of them. Agisillus felt like royalty himself standing in front of the beautifully built wagon with its gigantic wheels nearly reaching his chin. He tightened the belt around his tunic, standing up a little straighter. He remembered the caravan and the pampered boy from so long ago—this time he would be riding inside!

Lucius stepped out of the palace a few moments later with two soldiers in full armor and nodded at Agisillus. He didn't say a word. His lips were tight—perhaps he was questioning the risky decision he'd made the previous evening. A red cloak was thrown over his shoulders, and a sword strapped to his waist kept his leather vest tight around his uniform. It was a uniform that was much too fancy for battle, but the medals dangling from his cloak revealed a history of heroism and bravery, perhaps even against Gauls.

One of the soldiers held a torch near his face, illuminating Lucius's determined look as his eyes squinted and focused on organizing the scrolls in the compartment below the wagon doorway. There was immense pressure on him, as he himself would have to answer to the emperor of Rome soon. This may have been the reason he was so open to the Gaul's invention.

Agisillus hadn't slept all night. He'd lain awake as his mind raced over all that had transpired. One day he was being dragged in as a dirty prisoner with oversized clothing and the next he was headed out on a journey with the minister of agriculture. Perhaps his luck was starting to turn again, and this time he wasn't going to let it slip through his fingers.

They rode for hours in the dark, Agisillus was silent on the cushioned seat as Lucius and the soldier talked. The other two soldiers sat outside, holding the reins. He had been pleased to see that the fat one hadn't joined them on the journey. The man would have gladly found an opportunity to punish the Gaul who had been the cause of humiliation in front of his peers and his superior. Agisillus hoped he would not see him again.

They reached a new estate every few hours, and Lucius met with the overseer as the entire group walked into the fields to inspect the soil, the furrows, and the aqueducts built to bring water when there was a shortage of rain. None of the estates boasted a palace like Lucius, but they did share many common elements: hastily-constructed barns, a storehouse with a threshing floor manned by slaves dripping wet from the heat, huts that served as slaves' housing, and a larger building with living quarters for the overseer and the guards. And then miles and miles of poorly-cultivated wheat fields, often stretching up onto hillsides and down into valleys. Much of the land had yet to be cleared of grass, boulders, and trees.

The Romans were desperate, and in their desperation they had stretched themselves far and wide as they occupied the land. Now they were paying the price for their carelessness.

Agisillus hadn't said a word all day. They walked the fields and kicked at rocks and brush, and Lucius grew more frustrated. At one estate, late in the day, he stood looking over the fields, hands on his hips and belt strap, sweat rolling down his face in the heat of the sun.

"Perhaps I should have remained an officer and never taken on the position of the minister," he said under his breath. "Perhaps I'm not the right man for this job." Lucius looked defeated.

They had wandered a few hundred yards from the others, examining the fields. Agisillus finally spoke up.

"The problem is you have warriors trying to do the work of farmers," he said. "These fields are massive, but if you had properly cultivated fields that were a fraction of the size, they would be growing thick with good wheat."

Lucius looked at Agisillus quizzically for a few moments. "It was reported to me that you were arrested for being drunk and fighting in a tavern," he said. "And that you were a vagabond. How did you come up with that drawing of the furrow digger? It is a clever design coming from a homeless drunk. Where are you from?" Lucius was curious.

"A little village somewhere in Gallia Celtica," Agisillus replied.

Lucius cocked his head back in surprise. "We will be in that region soon—and do you have family there?"

Agisillus hesitated for a moment and then shook his head. "No." He hoped the man would not pry further.

"How does one from Gallia Celtica, a land of barbarians and poor crop farmers, have the imagination to design a tool such as yours?"

Agisillus searched for a response. He was not comfortable sharing with the man the dream that had been sparked by the boy in the fancy wagon, and he noticed with relief the man was not waiting for an answer. Lucius stood and observed the fields.

Finally he clapped his hands together as if to snap his mind to attention and turned to head for the wagon. "It is time for us to go," he said. "The nearest town with a blacksmith is hours away, and we need to get there before nightfall."

Agisillus immediately recognized the same fascinating

roads winding through the thick forest which they walked through only days ago when he was a prisoner. They were headed straight for the town in which he'd been arrested. How far would they go after that? Would he see Vectimarius again? He so wanted to explain himself to the generous barkeep who had kept him alive and given him an opportunity to change.

During the long ride Lucius had explained his plan—to meet and reconcile with the Gauls. It was his last attempt at keeping another war from breaking out and preventing famine.

Because they had failed to produce enough with their own fields, the harsh reality was that the Romans would have to take crops and grain from the Gauls, either by force or by forced labor— and that would only be a temporary solution. It would still never be enough. The Oracles had predicted this famine would last for years.

But now things could be changing. They could forge Agisillus's tool and have the blacksmiths sell them to the farmers; the farmers could increase the size of their fields and duplicate their efforts, keep what they needed to live on, and sell the surplus to the Romans by contract. The most difficult part of the plan, Lucius predicted, would be to convince the emperor, Caesar himself, that the plan was sound—a challenging political task, especially after Caesar's gruesome defeat by the Gauls in the Battle of Gergovia many years ago.

This plan also could avoid much more violence and resistance, which would surely come if they were forced to take land from the Gauls.

Agisillus could hardly contain his emotions, shifting in his seat and constantly peeking out the window as they rode in silence in the wagon. His invention could save the Romans and the Gauls from another war! If Lucius's plan unfolded the way he hoped it would, could he really help save Rome from the famine? He wished his mother and father could see him now, and he hoped they were watching from heaven, or wherever God took the dead. Here he was sitting next to and advising a man who shared meals with the emperor!

It was a bumpy ride, and the wagon jerked violently on occasion when it hit a pothole or rock in the road. Only the sound of creaking wood against the steel straps, holding the beautifully shaved oak slats of the wagon together, was louder than the horse hooves on the beaten road.

Agisillus's thoughts drifted to the tavern, and something the traveler had said that evening struck him now as they rode.

"People dream up things which the Creator would gladly fulfill, but they are so distracted, impatient, unbelieving, and easily discouraged, that when they are given the very thing they once asked for, they become like cowards simply because their dream comes disguised as a setback and is never easily achieved."

He had been a coward, abandoning his dreams quickly when the challenges arose. This time, however, he had taken action. Maybe he was finally becoming like the diligent farmer.

***

He had fallen asleep with his face tucked into his elbow but woke once the cart wheels hit the cobblestone. Torches lit their way as they rode through the town, turned up a side street, and came to a stop at the stables behind an inn. It was Gorgiva, the same town he had been arrested in. As soon as they entered the inn through the back door, he realized it was the same inn he'd stayed in on the night of the fight.

He wondered if the innkeeper would remember him, but then remembered his oiled hair and fitted tunic. Nobody would recognize him here. He winced as he imagined the fate of the cart he'd left out back.

Upstairs, the soldier closed the door behind him but Agisillus heard no footsteps walking away. His door would be guarded overnight.

He plopped on the cushioned bed, pulled the candle closer, tugged at the leather strings to remove the fourth scroll, and stretched it out in front of him.

Scroll 4 The Harvest

4:1 The diligent farmer hires helpers, and they gather the harvest. He fills the storehouses he has built, loads his carts with sacks and barrels, and the caravan heads to the village to sell the excess for profit.

The wise reap bountifully—on harvest day, the work of their hands is revealed. What was done in private is brought to the light. Now the world will see who labored and persisted, and who sat with hands folded when not a soul was watching. The wise are rewarded for their labor. Fools are bitter with envy and humiliation when their laziness is revealed.

4:2 Leaving the market, the diligent farmer holds tightly to his satchel as it rings with the sound of coins. The heavy satchel is a burden he carries proudly. His family is at home waiting and he is eager to bring it to them; they were the driving force behind his relentless labor.

The wise do not strive to gain wealth for the love of the money; they labor diligently, knowing that wealth will provide freedom. They earn money in order to live life on their own terms and spend their days on things that are important to them. Fools become slaves to money because to them, a satchel full of coins means status and material possessions. They neglect the most treasured things in life in pursuit of money and wither to old age, dying with no family, no friends, and still no money.

4:3 The diligent farmer teaches his employees the secrets to possessing a heavy satchel of coins. It does not bother him if they listen to the wisdom and apply it or not—he continues to teach and knows that some will listen and some simply won't.

The wise do not lose sleep over the poverty of fools; they understand wisdom flows freely, available to all, but only those who open their ears will become wise. Fools fight indecision, seek shortcuts, don't believe in what is available to them, and finally conclude "money is the root of all evil," when they can't find a way to earn it.

4:4 The diligent farmer long ago learned the secret of giving: when he had little, he still gave from what he had to those who were needy, but to the lazy neighbors who were able and healthy, he gave nothing.

The wise remain wealthy because they respect money. It draws near to them and stays with them, because they understand the language of it. The more they give, the more they receive, but they do not simply throw it to the wind. Fools stare with longing eyes and demand the wealthy be generous, but they do not wish to understand why they are poor, and in poverty they will remain. Even if much were given to them, it would soon dissipate.

4:5 The diligent farmer is admired. He is respected everywhere he goes, and when he speaks, silence falls over those around him. His wisdom is cherished by those who want the same for their lives. He has become everything they wish to be, and he inspires many, not merely by his talk, but by the way he lives. He is able to give to the world much more than he has taken from it.

The seed, which is the gift of God, is an investment when it falls into the hands of the wise, because from little they create much. Fools devour the seed before it is planted and produce no fruit; God's gifts are often wasted because of the way foolish men live.

4:6 The diligent farmer invites all who would listen to his celebration. He shares stories of his struggles, stories of his dreams, stories of his perseverance and faith, and he teaches about the goodness of life and all God has done for him. The student has become the teacher, thus completing the circle of life.
The wise create disciples from a life well-lived. Their life is a lamppost in the dark, showing the way to prosperity, purpose, happiness, and wealth for a wanderer to find his way. Fools do not tend to the garden, which is their mind. They neither live nor die well, and their children perpetuate their folly.

4:7 The diligent farmer, at the end of his days, lies in a bed of honor with a smile upon his face. When he passes on to the other side, he is full of joy because he finally meets his creator.
The wise look back upon a life worth living. Fools become frantic as the end approaches, grasping at their final moments as they remember a life filled with regrets.

Those with eyes to see and ears to hear, let them see and hear!

A life of regrets. Agisillus knew he had been given a second chance, but these words stung. He stared at the plank ceiling above his bed. His luck had turned again, but in the dark of the night, the weight of the unknown was unbearable. He noticed it was always this way—in the day, one's troubles were tolerable; at night, they were magnified. He was desperate for the next day to begin. He was desperate to live like the diligent farmer. He was desperate to produce a return on the traveler's investment in him.

Chapter 8
The Orator Speaks

Agisillus fiddled with the belt around his tunic as Lucius and the blacksmith huddled over the sketch spread across the table a few yards away. The blacksmith glanced back at Agisillus and the two soldiers who stood with him in the doorway of the shop. With a snarl that came from deep within his jiggling belly, the shop owner silenced the busy forgers who had been hammering away nearby. The hammering stopped, and the loud hiss of red-hot iron being dipped into buckets of water filled the shop as steam rose all around. Agisillus had loved the process during his short time as a forger: pulling the iron out of

119

the blazing stove; hammering; shaping it to a hoe, a blade, or whatever else had been ordered; cooling it quickly; and repeating the process to final perfection.

At times, however, the job was more than he could handle. Sometimes he would knock the iron out of his own hand with the heavy hammer or shower the nearest forger with scalding flakes, then rush to help the frantic chap brush them off. He was slow to learn the craft and spent more time dreaming up his own tool designs than actually working. But he missed the familiar sights and smells.

The tall soldier seemed to have warmed to him and offered him a draw on his pipe as they stood waiting, which Agisillus respectfully declined. He enjoyed the smell of tobacco and had tried it once when his father let him take a puff from his pipe, but then it burned his lungs until he thought he'd suffocate. He coughed for what seemed like an eternity with both palms on his knees, trying to recover. Hearing his father's hearty laughter gave him hope the pain would subside. The smell of the burning pipe filled him with nostalgia, along with a little nausea.

He tugged on his belt, his fists squeezed around the thick leather, and shifted from one leg to the other. This was agonizing. The longer they took, the more his mind floated in the familiar direction of doubt. Maybe the blacksmith would refuse to forge the tool. Maybe it wouldn't be as useful in the fields as he hoped it would be. Maybe Lucius would grow impatient if they had trouble getting the tool forged. And maybe Lucius would change his mind and the whole plan would fall through; the man was clearly under immense pressure.

Finally, the blacksmith and Lucius shook hands. An

agreement! He turned to the three, and a quick smile flashed across his usually serious face.

Agisillus let out a silent sigh of relief. He had hoped they wouldn't be faced with hostility—a Gaul working alongside the Romans in occupied territory—but knew things would only worsen between the Romans and Gauls in the months to come if this plan wasn't accomplished. It felt strange and exciting at once to be standing among the Romans as a peer.

"We have our agreement. Dosso, the blacksmith, will contact forgers in the neighboring towns to begin building the furrow diggers," Lucius said as they approached the wagon. "Then the Republic of Rome will provide the furrow diggers at no expense to any farmer who agrees to expand his fields to grow crops under contract to Rome, whether Roman or Gaul."

Agisillus tried hard to keep from smiling. He felt like shouting at the top of his lungs with joy. He jumped ahead of Lucius and reached to open the wagon door for the man.

"We will have to earn their trust if these farmers are to cooperate," Lucius continued as he nodded toward Agisillus and climbed in. "There is still so much animosity, but we do not have another choice. We had success with this one blacksmith, but we now have to reach every forger and farmer in the land for this plan to be effective. We've got to duplicate and delegate."

He pointed at Agisillus. "You, my friend, have a larger task at hand."

Agisillus's mind scrambled as he followed Lucius into the wagon. *Aren't I done? What else does Lucius need from me? Does he want me to come up with more tools?*

Lucius climbed into the front of the wagon. "We will

discuss it further this evening," he said.

All day the wagon bounced along the roads from town to town, passing through smaller villages made up of just a few families. Just as dusk was settling in, the driver turned the wagon onto a side road and headed up a hill overlooking the entirety of a large town below.

Agisillus could see hundreds of torches glimmering from a distance. As they descended and got closer, he realized the looming shadow on which the torches floated was not a town but the exterior walls of a fort. The four walls were the height of several men standing on one another's shoulders and were made up of shaved logs dug in vertically, held together by steel straps and sharpened into a point to prevent a breach.

A whining creak pierced the evening dusk as the massive gates slowly opened and the wagon pulled into an open area in the compound.

They had reached the final Roman outpost that separated Roman-occupied Gaul and the wild country extending to the north. The Roman army's campaigns had ceased at this very point, and the outpost was now used as housing for patrols and reinforcements when skirmishes between Gaul rebels and Romans broke out. Several white and red-striped officer tents lined the center of the fortified post, while infantrymen slept in smaller identical tents around the perimeter.

They entered the largest tent, the officers' quarters, and Agisillus could hardly imagine the effort it must have taken to lug in the elegant furnishings—from the thick woven carpet, to the military flags swinging from the roof nearly thirty feet in the air, to the stretched wolf and bear hides on the walls—undoubtedly personal trophies. The tent was brightly lit by dozens of oil torches burning from bronze bowls, which filled the room with a sweet scent. Drapes divided the space into separate rooms.

Just inside was a short cedar table on which sat a strange vase, similar to one Agisillus had seen in the hut of a Druid. Several men had been reclining on cushions around the table and immediately jumped to their feet when Lucius entered the room. While they were dressed down, only partially in uniform, Agisillus knew they were officers by the three patches on their vests.

They simultaneously shouted "Ave!" and threw their arms out sharply with a salute. Agisillus stood nervously as the men exchanged greetings; they hardly noticed the skinny Gaul dressed in Roman attire lurking near the entrance.

Hours went by as the men reclined on the cushions that circled the table, discussing politics and taking turns puffing from a large pipe attached to the vase with a hose. Agisillus politely declined each time someone offered the pipe to him. The burning substance in the pipe had a sharp smell when it hit his nostrils, and he was sure it was not ordinary tobacco. He had already become light-headed just sitting next to the men as they exhaled.

One of the men pointed at Agisillus. "Lucius, your helper has the eyes of the savages!" he said and laughed hard as the others chuckled along. "You've been infiltrated by the enemy!" Agisillus's heart pounded so loudly, he wondered if they all could hear it. He tried to smile as he stole a glance at Lucius. Lucius was still reading a report he was handed upon arrival and without looking up casually stated, "He is a Gaul."

For what seemed to be a lifetime, the room went silent but for the sound of the tent walls flapping gently in the wind.

Agisillus felt every eye in the room staring at him, not

daring to look at any of them. The flames of the torches bounced in the room, and he hoped his tunic was covering the lump in his throat.

"Agisillus is a brilliant chap who nearly drank himself into the ground, and the world will be better because he did not." Lucius exhaled a ring of smoke but never lifted his eyes.

Hearing Lucius speak on his behalf and defend him in that terrifying moment moved Agisillus, and he fought back tears.

"If we had someone like him in my position, perhaps we wouldn't be where we are now, months away from a famine that could cause Rome much suffering." Lucius spoke in a low voice and with authority, finally looking up from the report.

"We've got a plan because of him. Even if his tool is not as effective as we expect, even if we can't get the masses to support what we are trying to do, it will have been worth the effort. I'm willing to take the chance and see where this takes us, because, as leaders, we have let this crisis come upon us with little attempt at preventing it. The time to pit savages against noblemen is over. We will all be fools equally if we fail."

He looked directly at the man who had insulted Agisillus: "I understand—you have seen the vicious side of these people and have lost men at the tip of their swords. But you must remember where you are now. You are not in Rome. You have made a home for yourself on their land and by the spilling of their blood. You are on the land of their ancestors . . . and why? So that the emperor can further engrave his name in the history books?" Lucius spit on the ground with disgust, never taking his eyes off the officer.

"I will give the emperor credit, however; he has finally become wise to the fact that another war with the Gauls would be fatal. We are turning our attention to protecting our people now. I am here on his authority. Surely you have already received your orders to abandon your post as soon as it is safe enough for you to pull back?"

The officer nodded.

Lucius continued, "As the first order of business, I need a patrol of thirty men to accompany me on my journey and another thirty to accompany Agisillus. The further north we go, the more protection we may need—even if we are extending an olive branch, we may be met with hostility."

Agisillus sat up and moved to the edge of his seat. Did Lucius just say thirty men would accompany him? He immediately began to worry.

Where am I going, and why would I be going without the minister? He did not want to leave Lucius's side. Especially since all these soldiers openly hated Gauls.

The conversation between Lucius and the officers continued as Agisillus debated in his mind but his ears perked up when Lucius began talking about the blacksmith:

"The blacksmith I spoke with today wisely brought to my attention that simply providing a tool to the farmers may not be convincing enough. As you understand, we've got to prove to the farmers there is an opportunity at hand. Sure, some will listen, and others will be skeptical and will do everything in their power to undermine the Republic, but what I need this young man to do is petition on our behalf, to stand in the gap between Rome and Gaul. They will be more likely to listen to their own."

Agisillus stared at the minister, the blood rushing out of his face. None of this had been mentioned before.

"You will put together a message, and you will have to become quite the orator, young man, because the survival of Rome and all of Gaul will depend on it." He spoke directly to Agisillus now.

"What are you proposing?" the officer asked Lucius. "Do you believe that the savages will actually grow crops to feed Rome?"

"Yes," Lucius replied sharply. "I have witnessed firsthand what forced labor brings—nothing but a few sacks of wheat from each field. It is ineffective, and we have no time for other options. The Gauls have fertile land, but they also have the manpower and farming experience. If we extend this war and begin to take their crops, there will never be enough—they grow only enough to feed themselves. But if we persuade them to grow tenfold what they grow now, there will be plenty for their families *and* they can earn profit for the excess they sell to us."

Lucius spoke loudly and sternly, the veins in his neck protruding as he laid out his plan.

"Be wise, open your ears, and hear me. This is why I need him," he said, grabbing Agisillus by the shoulder. "Not only has he been raised a farmer, his invention will help the Gauls expand their fields and prepare them so that even the smallest of villages can be prosperous. One ox pulling this tool can do the work of ten men hoeing the fields by hand."

Lucius looked each of the officers in the eye as he gave his final order. "Get me that patrol."

Agisillus had dreamed of doing something extraordinary, but he could never quite imagine how it would come to be. Here he was experiencing the moment of a lifetime. What would have happened if he'd never jumped up to speak with Lucius?

How quick I have been to give up, he thought. *How many opportunities did I miss along the way? How many times could my life have changed for the better if I had committed to trying even if I were scared or discouraged? I often said no, waiting for a better opportunity, but how much more difficult is it to say yes to an opportunity when one has already declined once before?*

It was much scarier to imagine where his life would have ended up if he hadn't jumped up to speak to Lucius, than to imagine the fears he would soon have to face.

Chapter 9
Final Farewell

Agisillus stared at the blank scroll before him and the jar of ink, the thick liquid, black as coal, with a feather dipped into it.

"Speak with authority," Lucius had told him. "Use your voice and use your body to display confidence even when you don't feel confident inside—the greatest orators of Rome do this. You won't have much time to hold their attention, so do not give all of the details; do not try to convince them to help *Rome*. Instead, paint for them a picture of what this decision can do for their families, for their people, for their nation."

Agisillus felt sick. There was no way he could possibly stand in front of a crowd of people and speak. The last few years had only made him less social and confident. And public speaking was not something he would have been able to do well even before his life fell apart.

"Show them how they can become a prosperous people and rise above the plague of poverty. There are no limits on the money Romans can pay, and it will always find other nations to exploit. That's the way it has always been, but if you Gauls agree to this peace offering, to this partnership, this moment will go down in history as the turning point of your nation and its people."

Later, he sat alone in a humble tent, lit by the candlelight. His palms were already sweating at the mere thought of speaking to an entire village of people who by all accounts were more successful than he ever was. They had families, they had community, they had farms and huts, shops and fishing businesses, and here he was—a vagabond, a thief, a drunkard, a Roman prisoner— expected to speak about an opportunity for prosperity. He couldn't bring himself to believe in Lucius's idea.

Though he was the owner of the precious scrolls of the diligent farmer, he was merely a student of their philosophy and in no way a practitioner. He was the inventor of a tool that was soon going to be hammered and molded in every blacksmith shop in the land, but this had only come to be most recently.

And it didn't yet exist.

He thought about telling Lucius to find someone else for the job but remembered the promise he'd made to himself earlier in the evening. He had sworn he would never again make a decision out of fear, because every moment could be carrying a seed of greater purpose from God himself, and he couldn't afford to miss it.

He dipped the feather into the jar and applied it to the scroll.

Once Agisillus began to write, he did not stop. The hand bearing the feather seemed to move on its own, from the jar to the scroll, back and forth it went. His life story unfolded before his eyes and every emotion came back to him as he put his entire journey into the speech. Every memory, the bad and the good, spilled out on the sheets in front of him. His thoughts had been etched into the words now drying in the candlelight. At times his hand shook so badly he had to stop as the emotion swept over him. He wiped the tears from his swollen eyes over and over again, drying his palms on his tunic.

Why had he, the one who gave up on *everything*, been given so many chances? God had been so patient, and he was grateful that even though he had done nearly everything in his power to destroy this gift, God had not given up on him. This must have been that *love, grace, and mercy*, three ideas his father so often talked about, three of God's greatest qualities.

He understood now the task was much greater than just his own dream of riches. He became aware of the subtle secrets in the proverbs as they continually nudged the philosophy of God's greater purpose for man. They revealed a deep truth—that when a man receives from God a seed, it does not only carry the secrets to that man's own purpose and success within it but always produces a harvest that flows beyond his reach, so that inevitably the man begins to affect and change the world by simply pursuing his own dream. Just like a fruit from one tree does not produce just one seed to pass on but, instead, produces many.

The Romans had many gods, the Druids had their spirits,

but Agisillus had begun to believe in the God of the diligent farmer, the God of the traveler, the God of his father and mother. A Creator that was eager to walk alongside his creation, every painful and joyous step of the way.

How he wished he could once again come face to face with the traveler from the tavern and embrace him.

For days Agisillus walked the walls of the fort with speech in hand, reading it aloud. He would stop and emphasize every word, using his hands to motion wide as he rehearsed each line like Lucius had shown him. He would step into each word, loudly repeating it until it sounded natural to say. He would stop and speak to the log walls of the fort, looking from log to log as if they were faces in the crowd, to practice using eye contact.

It was embarrassing at first when soldiers would stroll by, but soon he was so engrossed into his rehearsal that he hardly noticed them. He wanted to memorize each word, so that even when the fear of standing before the crowd would surely shake him, he could continue to speak.

Lucius wanted to be present for the first speech to ensure all went well, and Agisillus was thankful, although the minister's presence did not help calm his nerves like he had hoped it would.

At their first stop, the word was spread throughout the village, and the people gathered. They were curious. Agisillus ducked behind a hut and vomited. His hands trembled, and he wondered if the massive lump in his throat would prevent him from speaking. The larger the crowd grew, the more frequently he glanced down the road of the village, trying hard to keep from sprinting far away so he would not have to do this. He feared the villagers would mock him or worse, attack him for being a traitor and working with the Romans. Angry mobs were impossible to contain, even if he had thirty soldiers with him.

He closed his eyes and prayed once again, this time seeing in his mind the man from the tavern, seeing the diligent farmer with his hands raised to the sky from his fields, and feeling God right there next to him.

A strange thing happened just as Lucius called him up to the makeshift platform used by street entertainers. He stood and looked out at the enormous crowd, his legs shaking. But as he opened his mouth to begin his story, a peace came over him. It seemed like the more he used his body and the motions he had rehearsed at the fort, the more confident he felt. Lucius had told him this would happen.

"When the body is making the small and restricted movements and motions of a person who is afraid, the mind responds accordingly and becomes full of fear. But when you force your body to act as if you are confident—plant your feet, steady your hand on a hip, hold your head high—then your mind will respond accordingly and become confident," Lucius had said.

"Every good officer has learned to be in control of his emotions this way so that he can be courageous on the battlefield, even when he is deathly afraid."

Moving from edge to edge on the platform, spreading his hands wide as if he were painting each word, Agisillus experienced what he thought a few days earlier would be impossible.

The eyes of each villager, young and old, followed his every move. They hung onto his words. When he finished, much to his surprise, the stoic villagers approached him one by one, as if ashamed to be falling for a trick but wanting badly to believe it was true.

Some asked which village he was from, others questioned if he were truly a Gaul, while others wondered if Rome could really be trusted to pay. He was pleased to learn many had already heard of the predicted famine—and he remembered how quickly bad news could spread between these little villages.

A line formed at the blacksmith shop, and the blacksmith busily recorded each family name and farmer requesting to be placed on the list for Agisillus's new furrow digger.

"We must keep moving," Lucius said as they rode in the wagon. "Not all will be as welcoming as the people today, but we must deliver the message, nonetheless. I have already ordered a decree to be posted in every town and village before we arrive, so that people know what is coming and will come to hear you. This will help the message spread, but it is still critical that you stop in each town, because as you've witnessed, the message will more likely be received if it is coming from you. Did you notice how attentively they listened to you? Powerful!"

Agisillus blushed and heaved a huge sigh of relief. He always had trouble accepting compliments—not that he had received many in the last few years—but was filled with gratitude. The anxiety and worry leading up to the moment on the platform had given him a headache. But he felt confident now that even though he would be just as nervous each time, he would be able to get through the speech. In fact, he was sure of it.

When they arrived back at the fort, Lucius stepped inside his tent and emerged shortly with a leather pouch neatly sealed with a thin lace. He offered it to Agisillus.

Agisillus took it in his palm and immediately noticed its unusual weight. It was disproportionally heavy for a small pouch, and he heard a jingling. Coins. But why would Lucius give him money?

"What is this for?" he asked, still holding out his hand. "Payment," the man replied plainly. "P-payment?" Agisillus stammered. His eyebrows shot up, but he quickly tried to conceal his surprise.

"It is payment for fulfilling your duties to the Roman Republic, for services rendered as a public orator. Orators are subject to great challenges and responsibilities. They can move people to action. They can inspire people to change, to do things differently. They can sway public opinion for good or for evil. They can lead a nation to victory or defeat. Great orators will always be handsomely rewarded. You will, too, if you continue to master your craft and do what obviously comes naturally to you."

Lucius slowed his words and lowered his voice as he stepped closer to Agisillus, placing a hand on his shoulder.

"I saw it in you the day you were brought in with that other miserable derelict, Agisillus. I've been to many nations, I've seen many people, I've traveled to worlds you wouldn't believe existed, and one thing remains true everywhere: it is not just the people of strong empires, like Rome, that are smarter, wiser, and more blessed or gifted. As much as we enjoy believing so, it just is not true. From my experience, there are incredible people in every tribe and nation, from every class and economic background, be they rich or poor. And the only difference between the ones who prosper and those who remain in poverty is what they believe themselves to be in that small space between their ears." Lucius tapped Agisillus's forehead.

"You are nothing like the Gauls I routinely deal with. I can see their hatred for me and everything Rome stands for in their eyes. Savages are what they act like, savages are what they will be treated as, and savages are what they will always remain. You had something else in your eyes the day you arrived, something I can't explain. A deeper sense of purpose, as if you had had an encounter with . . ." He paused for a moment and looked past Agisillus.

"I wasn't sure of it until you showed me your sketch, but I believe you were brought here for such a time as this. Perhaps this is a divine intervention; perhaps it is Rome's last chance to turn away from evil, from the war they have brought into many nations. I am sure of it now; there is someone up there, watching over us."

Lucius hesitated, as if debating to say what he wanted to say, before continuing.

"I noticed the dirty clothing and the smell of alcohol on you that day. I've seen it before—sometimes it is the most brilliant of minds and the greatest of dreamers that end up as drifters, because they once had something inside that was bursting at the seams, and yet they could not be the person they needed to become.

"I'm just glad to see you held on to hope all these years."

Lucius had noticed Agisillus's head drop. With one hand, Agisillus desperately tried to wipe his tears as quickly as they flowed, and the other clutched the sack of coins. It contained more coins than he had ever seen in his life.

Lucius squeezed the thin, drooping shoulders of Agisillus for a moment and then walked into his tent.

***

The wheels rattled along the winding roads. The further they rode into the territory of Gaul, the worse the roads became.

Gaul and the Roman Empire were separated by hundreds

of miles of thick mountainous pine forests and wild country that not many foreigners were willing to trek. But after the wars had begun, these slave-built roads eased travel as the Roman army eventually fought its way deep into the territory.

The sound of the horses' hooves clicking in unison along the hardened dirt drew the passengers into a trance. The two soldiers who accompanied Agisillus inside of the wagon reclined on thick cotton-stuffed cushions laid across the benches.

Two more sat on the roof of the wagon holding the reins and never running out of conversation topics or coarse jokes.

He studied the two soldiers in the wagon. Both had removed their chest armor for the ride, but he had noticed the markings on their uniforms—both were centurions. He found it odd the centurions would travel alone, they were typically leading groups of men, but then remembered Lucius had sent for a unit of auxiliary men to join them along the way.

The Roman army recruited auxiliary soldiers from non-Roman tribes. They assisted the Roman legionary troops with extra manpower and fought with specialized techniques in areas unfamiliar to the Romans. They received Roman citizenship when they completed their service, which often made them more barbaric in battle, hungry for the rewards they would reap, should they live long enough to retire. Agisillus assumed the two centurions would take charge of the auxiliary that would accompany them.

It was unnerving to think they might ride through areas which still contained pockets of resistance, and he anxiously watched out the window, praying they would not run into trouble.

One of the centurions plucked the cork from a flask hanging around his neck and took a swig, grimacing from the bite of the liquor. He lifted the string over his head and handed the flask to Agisillus, who took it without hesitation and swallowed a mouthful. The strong drink burned his throat, and he breathed in heavily through his nostrils and out his mouth, trying to ease the sting. Both of the centurions laughed hard.

"They don't make it like this in Rome!" one centurion said as he took a second swig. "The Gauls can brew a drink."

Agisillus took another sip. He immediately felt lighter and relaxed his shoulders, reclining back into the soft cushion on his elbow. He questioned himself for a moment— perhaps he was getting too comfortable in his new environment—but then decided to go ahead. The centurions had been exchanging drinking stories, and he began sharing his.

"About a year ago, I was in a pub and drank just a bit more than I could handle and fell asleep. I still do not know to this day what had transpired, perhaps the batch had too much old honey in it, but when I woke up, I was out in the street—the barkeep must have dragged me out. I was still drunk, and I shouted something at a patrol walking by, and when they came at me, I tried to run . . . I got just a few yards away before the ground came up out of nowhere and hit me. I did not realize I was falling and did not lift my hands to stop my face from hitting the dirt . . ."

Both centurions began laughing and Agisillus continued.

"They kicked me hard and only stopped when I threw up on one of their feet!"

"Just don't throw up here in the wagon," one centurion said with a chuckle, and the three of them laughed.

Sharing a little humor helped ease the anxious and awkward ride, and reminded him of how much had changed for him.

Night had fallen, and the wagon slowed as they pulled into a field at the side of the road. After lighting a fire, the soldiers spread sheepskins on the mossy ground. The two riders would stay on guard, taking turns sleeping and staying awake through the night.

One centurion spread his sheepskin inside of the wagon; the other two men lay down next to the fire. Agisillus grabbed the sheepskin he was given and crawled beneath the wagon, in between the two front wheels. If there was dew in the morning, at least his head and shoulders would stay dry. His feet were just a few feet from the fire and kept the rest of his body warm. He was snoring in a few minutes.

Agisillus jerked awake to the cold steel pressed against his throat.

"Well, boy, you have come to the end of your little fantasy quest," a throaty voice snarled. Agisillus recognized it. He could hear the labored breathing in between words and remained still, trying to keep the blade from digging further into his skin. He would have known the voice anywhere. It was Faustus, the fat, bitter soldier from Lucius's palace, clearly winded from bending down on one knee to reach for Agisillus under the wagon. Two strong arms wrapped around Agisillus's shoulders and dragged him to his feet.

His eyes eventually adjusted to the night, and he saw an entire unit of Roman soldiers, perhaps twenty of them, staring back at him with torches burning. The flickering light from the torches bounced off of the massive trees surrounding the field, throwing ghostly shadows onto the looming trunks.

Agisillus helplessly watched as Faustus handed a note to one of the centurions. The centurion read the note and the two conversed in low voices before the centurion spoke up, this time loud enough for Agisillus to hear from where he was being held.

"Why would Lucius wait until now to change his plan?" the centurion asked. "We've been riding for more than a day!"

The fat soldier snapped a few sharp words and reached back for the note. Agisillus could not quite catch the words, but the centurion looked at Agisillus as he listened. Finally, he nodded and saluted Faustus, who turned and marched toward Agisillus. He wrapped a rope around the young man's wrists.

Something must have happened. Had Lucius, the man who was so gracious to him, changed his mind? Why would he have these men catch up with them all the way here in these forests, so deep in Gaul territory, just to arrest Agisillus again? If he had changed his mind, did he really need this entire unit of men to do his bidding? Agisillus's mind raced as he tried to keep up with the pace of the horseman he was tied to.

Faustus rode up on his horse and slowed it to the pace of their walk.

"Your savior Lucius never sent for you, boy!" he laughed and leaned in closer. "But this little idea of his to save Rome by befriending Rome's enemies is a fantasy. So I have taken it upon myself to put an end to this plan for world peace," he snarled.

"You barbarians have given us enough trouble and won't get off so easy, let alone be paid by the taxes of Roman citizens! I'll see to it myself that the only way this war ends is not by Rome paying you dogs for your crops but you and all your people working for Rome as slaves . . . that is, those of you who survive the sword."

Agisillus clenched his jaw. His mouth was suddenly dry, and he had to keep himself from ripping at the ropes tied around his wrists. The fat soldier seemed to be enjoying himself, but the more he spoke, the more Agisillus cursed him under his breath.

"By the time morning comes, we will sound the trumpets, and Lucius will have no choice but to step aside and let the men do what they do best. He'll be back to taking in the slaves we send him, and he'll continue to play with his pitiful fields. We will take what we need and not hand over a single denarius to you Gauls for it." He laughed, kicked his horse with his ankles, and trotted to the front of the line.

Agisillus wished the horse would shake him off and stomp him to death.

***

He struggled to keep his eyes from shutting as he stumbled hour after hour behind the horse. The night was cold and he shivered. He noticed they were not headed back toward Roman territory but continuing farther into Gaul instead.

Faustus had planned a raid on a town known to harbor Gaul warriors, in order to provoke a violent response. Lucius could never convince the emperor to restrain from war if skirmishes began, and with the months passing, he would have no choice but to invade and conquer to keep Rome from starving.

They eventually stopped to rest after nearly an entire night of marching. The soldiers huddled around several fires as the sky began to brighten over the horizon.

Agisillus sat with his head in his arms, slumped against a tree. The sun peeked through the tall trees, and as its rays warmed him, his shaking shoulders calmed to a shiver.

He remembered the scrolls and how the farmer ran to the field being destroyed by hail and wind. Agisillus was certainly in the midst of his own hailstorm. It seemed like a dream, these last few weeks . . . or months. He wasn't sure how long it had been since he was first arrested outside that tavern, but now just like the farmer, his unbelievable luck had run dry overnight.

What game was God playing now, giving him hope and a promising future only to take it away once again?

In his darkest hour, the diligent farmer rose to his feet and began to faithfully mend what was broken, to dig and to save what were left of his crops, and he kept his faith that the one who had given life to the seeds would give life again.

Perhaps I will get another chance. If what the traveler promised was true, God will hold up to his end of the deal. He has to—I have done all I possibly could.

He could see the town in the distance as the road left the forest and dropped steeply, winding down the open plains and leveling out in the valley far below. Smoke was rising from chimneys and shops, windmills spun slowly in the wind, and the poor fools were oblivious to the trouble headed their way. Agisillus's heart raced—he wanted to scream a warning.

During the Roman-Gallic Wars, the Romans went on raids and often left entire towns burning to the ground, taking all survivors as slaves. Now, Agisillus saw the terrible stories he heard growing up coming back to life. The soldiers passed flasks of their strong drink. Their helmets were strapped, chest armor tightened, and their banter subsided. They were ready for war.

Just as they were nearing the first few buildings of town, however, Agisillus started jumping up and down, not sending a warning, but shouting with relief.

Instead of the townspeople emerging to defend themselves, out from the side streets marched what seemed to be a thousand heavily-armed Roman soldiers. In the midst of them, seated high on his horse, shoulders draped in a bright scarlet cape, was Lucius.

He was dressed for battle, the red crest high on top of his helmet. He sat stone-faced and never took his eyes off Faustus for even a moment. He drew his sword and pointed it directly at the man as the army pulled to a stop but remained silent.

All watched as the traitor was tied and laid, enormous belly down, on a cart. He would be dealt with harshly. Agisillus had heard of the brutal punishment carried out on traitors to the empire. He'd even heard they were crucifying men, hanging them on crosses to die in the hot sun.

Lucius grabbed Agisillus's wrist and placed the ring that one of the soldiers had just slipped off Faustus's finger into his palm. Worn only by the highest-ranking officials, it bore the likeness of the emperor, and there were wheat branches engraved around the outline of the head. It was the gold signet ring of the minister of agriculture.

As it was much too large to fit on any of his bony fingers, he looped it on a string and hung it around his neck.

"With that ring, you answer to no one but the emperor and me," Lucius said, his voice calm now after dealing with Faustus. Agisillus was sure Lucius was going to kill the man when he saw the minister's white-knuckled grip on the sword, and he knew Lucius was barely holding himself back from carrying out the fatal swing as the fat man begged for mercy. Agisillus was glad Lucius restrained himself.

The soldiers went to work, marching like ants, and quickly erected a camp at the edge of town just off the main road. But Lucius and a few men along with Agisillus stayed in rooms at the inn. They dined at the pub as Lucius explained how he nearly missed the messenger carrying the centurion's message to him. He was headed out to the next village, but when he received word of the kidnapping, he organized his men and began the search for Agisillus.

After the meal, Agisillus stepped out and headed up the town's central road for a stroll. He walked from one end of the town to the other, admiring its buildings, connected roof-to-roof down each side of the street, with alleyways splitting every few buildings. He enjoyed the constant bustle of the townspeople going about their business. There was energy to it that made him feel not so alone.

He wondered if things would have turned out differently for him if he had been raised in a town like this instead of the little village he was born in. Perhaps his parents would not have had to work themselves to death. Perhaps they could have started a different business or trade here in a town where there seemed to be more possibilities and ambition. His father was smart; his mother was talented in anything she touched. But maybe this was the problem. Maybe staying busy was the very reason many people never followed their dreams. Perhaps trade work passed down from generation to generation was the reason people didn't discover new skills or talents.

After all, many people he knew were fisherman or farmers or blacksmiths simply because the trade had been in their family for generations.

Perhaps they never allowed themselves to expect more from life because they were led to believe they should be a blacksmith like their father was, or a fisherman like their grandfather was, or a seamstress like their mother was.

But if he lived in a town like this and had a comfortable life, would he have been available for the opportunities before him now? He would have carried on, perhaps gotten married and had children. But would he have been in the position to affect a pivotal moment like this, a moment like the coming famine, if all he had learned to do was earn a living for himself and his family? How can anyone impact the world if they only care for their own little universe?

The recent events had made him appreciate life now more than ever, but would he have had the same reverence for life if he had not experienced the lowest of lows?

What a terrible thing it was for God's greatest creation, human life, to be treated so wastefully. People admired seed, soil, sunshine, wind, earth, fire, and rain, mountains, seas, and skies, and yet they treated their own bodies and lives like oxen, fixed only on the work in front of them, shoulders to the plow as if nature were to be admired and human life was to be discarded.

Agisillus tugged sharply on his necklace. He picked up his pace as he walked. He would dedicate his life not only to making sure he was never poor again but also to making sure that anyone with ears to hear would hear how much more there was to experience in life.

The Gauls were on the brink of being wiped off the face

of the earth for their lack of wisdom and growth. But that would soon change. He would not rest until he helped even just one person wake up to his potential and truly begin to live.

He walked past a tavern but then stopped and pushed open the creaking oak door and took a seat at a table. It was a familiar place, but most taverns looked similar inside. There was always a fire going, a cauldron of stew hanging above it, thirsty patrons eager for a drink and a visit with old friends, and there were always the loyal customers, the ones the barkeep knew by name.

When his beer came, he held the mug tightly, appreciating its ability to ease his endless ruminating for a moment. He didn't worry about unwittingly overdrinking now; the emptiness of his old self had evaporated with his newfound purpose.

If only his father and mother could see him, the signet ring hanging from his neck, his completed invention, which was now being molded and hammered under the blazing fire of all the villages and towns in Gaul that Lucius had reached. The people back home could not understand his never-ending unease and desire for more from life, and they likely never would, but now he was alright with that. The need for people to understand him was gone. It had been replaced with a hunger to find the people seeking more from life, and to help them.

"Agisillus," a deep voice boomed. Two heavy hands landed hard on each shoulder, jostling his mug of beer. Startled, Agisillus turned, expecting trouble once again. But the face that looked back at him nearly made him weep with joy.

It was the stranger. The man whose conversation and gift

had transformed his life was standing before him.

The beard and the wild hair seemed to be more tamed now that they weren't whipped by snow and wind, but the eyes were just as dark and kind as he had remembered.

Agisillus tried to stand, but the man's embrace kept him down, and he quickly gave into it. It was only then that Agisillus caught a peculiar fragrance coming from the man. Strangely enough, the rugged man smelled of roses.

"I must have read every one of them a thousand times over. Thank you," he managed to choke out, fighting hard to keep the tears from rolling.

The traveler pulled the large satchel off of his back, dropped it on the floor under the table and waved for the barkeep. When he turned to face Agisillus, he spotted the signet ring around his neck and reached for it, pulling it in for a closer look and bringing Agisillus's entire body along with it.

His eyebrows raised then dropped as his face turned to a large grin.

"Do you know how many men and women like you I call on? How many I visit, traveling across seas and lands, looking for those who may prepare the way for me? And look at you—the sheep has heard the voice of the shepherd, and it will never stray again." The man spoke loudly, and every eye in the pub was on them now.

"Did you . . . did you seek me out intentionally?" Agisillus stammered, trying hard to understand.

"There is not a child, not a man, nor woman, nor any living thing on earth that I don't seek out intentionally," he said as he kept grinning.

"Sir, I still don't understand. Why did you choose to give me the scrolls that night long ago?"

The traveler replied loudly, almost as if to share the good

news with the entire tavern: "I have come to bring heaven to earth and all who are open to receive it shall receive it! Heaven is not only a faraway place for those who die; it is here, and it is now!

"Wise men sit and philosophize on things like heaven and the gods who dwell among them, yet it is men like the diligent farmer who actually see life's secrets revealed. It is not easy for those who have fixed their minds on the troubles before them—on lack, on suffering, on poverty—to understand. They cannot possibly see heaven when in their minds they have created hell."

Agisillus looked around to see if people were still watching, but everyone had carried on with their own conversations.

"When I saw you, so miserable, so lost, I saw a man who had created hell of his life, and I knew you were greatly in need of a little taste of heaven! Besides, you had already been seeking a better life; you just needed a little nudge. Your invention idea and your desire to provide a better life for your mother and father are admirable, and I will say it again, those who seek will find. Those who knock, a door will be opened for them. Those who ask for a thing will be given that thing."

The man seemed to be enjoying himself reciting those incredible words of wisdom once again for Agisillus. He paused for a moment and sipped his beer before continuing.

Agisillus did not want to miss another opportunity and quickly spoke up: "Who are you? What does it mean that you intentionally seek out every living thing?"

He blurted the questions as fast as they came to his head.

"The scrolls changed my life. I now know what seed was given to me! I now understand why I had big dreams when I was a child, why I envisioned a cart with a chest of gold inside, and why that desire nearly killed me on many occasions. But you are speaking now as if you are God himself, as if you know . . . *How* do you know? And what is your name? Where did the scrolls come from?"

He figured if he asked every question he had, the man would have no choice but to answer them one by one and could not leave until he did.

But the man stood up as soon as he was finished with his drink.

"I only wanted to see you once more, to embrace you once more, and this moment I will treasure until we meet again," he said as he pulled his bag over his shoulder.

"All of what you learned from the scrolls can be summarized into one sentence: *Whatever a man sees in his mind, does not doubt in his heart, and lives as if he has already received, will come to pass.* That is the secret most men will never understand. Remember this: heaven is here." He tapped Agisillus's temple.

"In here you can come to know the powers of heaven or the distress of hell. What you experience is up to you.

"For every one of your questions I answer, you will have ten more. But the wise do not become wise because they are given all the answers; the wise become wise because they have so many questions. You have the scrolls, Agisillus. They have secrets inside of them that you have not yet discovered. Each time you read them, more will be revealed to you. Do not seek hasty answers; instead, ask better questions. And then, pass the scrolls on to the next poor soul in need. You'll know who the right person is when you encounter them.

"You have been rewarded, but much more will be given to you, my good friend."

A smile spread across the traveler's face again. Agisillus jumped to his feet and grabbed the man's arm. "Sir . . .

who *are* you? You said I will see you again—when?"

The traveler paused for a long moment. His soul seemed to have momentarily left his body as his shoulders dropped and he stared at nothing in particular, still clutching his bag. Finally, he took a deep breath and sighed. "You may not see me again in the flesh, but you will hear of me. A day is coming on which many will hear my voice, though they will not see me with their eyes like you do now.

"I am the way, the truth, and the life. I am the bridge between man and God. Though they may not know it is me they seek, there is not a soul now, or 'til the end of time that will not desire what I have to give. Some will find me, and they will be transformed. But many will reject me because to a foolish man, the things of God are offensive. To a foolish man, the laws of the universe are a mystery. You are no fool, Agisillus. You will yet do greater things!" He clasped Agisillus's shoulders and squeezed them tightly.

Then he turned, walked out the door, and was gone.

Agisillus sat back down and did not touch his mug for what must have been an hour. What if he had missed all of this? He didn't want to imagine things turning out any differently than they had. As painful as it had been, he was a better man because of what he had endured.

He grabbed the pouch where he kept the scrolls and held it tight.

Suddenly he realized the strange traveler had forgotten to pay for his drink. Agisillus waved for the barkeep who made his way over.

"Sir, you can add his beer onto my tab—he must have been in a hurry." The barkeep looked at Agisillus quizzically.

"Who are you talking about?"

"The man, with the large bag and the long hair; the one who was sitting with me all this time—I believe he forgot to pay for his drink."

The tavern had been busy all evening; perhaps he could not keep track of every drink and trusted his patrons to pay.

The barkeep looked at Agisillus suspiciously. "Perhaps you've had one too many already," he said as he grabbed the two empty mugs off of the table. "I've been watching you talk to an empty chair all evening. If you start to scare away my customers, out you go," he said and went back to pouring beer.

Agisillus looked around the bar and then to the empty chair in front of him. Had no one else seen the traveler he sat with? Had he gone mad!? He quickly reached for his satchel and opened it—the scrolls were safe inside. He looked at the chair again and then slid to the side and peered underneath the table.

In front of the chair where the traveler had sat were two large footprints in the dust of the old wood floorboards, facing Agisillus. Next to them was the spot where the man had set his bag.

Agisillus smiled and then bit both lips hard as the tears he had been holding back began to flow. This time they did not stop. His shoulders shook, and he put his hand on his chin to steady himself so that no one would notice. Elbows on the table and palm to chin, Agisillus sipped his beer and sighed.

His heart was overflowing with joy, he had met God face to face, and he would never be the same again. Tomorrow he would see the village he'd sworn never to return to. Tomorrow he would return to a world he never expected to see again. Tomorrow the people of his little village would see the man who was once a drunkard return as a conqueror.

He would make sure that as long as he lived, he would do everything in his power to pull others from the gutters and salvage their lives. He would help them discover and plant their seeds.

His world would never be the same again. The whole world would never be the same again.

The fiddle brightened as the musicians picked up the pace. It was a lively tune, and the drunken men began to hoot and holler and clap along to the beat.

He stood curiously and walked closer to where the musicians sat and set his mug on a table near them. Perhaps it was his newfound success, perhaps it was the encounter with the strange traveler, or perhaps it was the beer which had gone to his head . . . but whatever it was, Agisillus felt a joy he'd never felt before. He planted his feet on the floorboards, crouched, threw his hands up in the air, and began to dance the silliest dance the world had ever seen. Everyone in the tavern cheered and clapped along to his stomping feet.

He had a smile on his face, a dream in his heart, and a secret he could not wait to give to the world.

The End

About the author

Michael was born in Soviet Russia, came to the United States just before the end of the Cold War as a political refugee, and is the grandson of a Siege of Leningrad and Dachau camp survivor. Today, Michael is a Game-Changing motivational speaker and Best-Selling author who has impacted thousands of people with his message of resilience, purpose, and hope. He is on a mission to help people discover a better way to live.

If you would like to have Michael speak at your corporate event, school, retreat, church, or any other event, please visit Michael's website here:

WWW.SPEAKLIFE365.COM

Other books by Michael V. Ivanov

The Mount of Olives:
11 Declarations to an Extraordinary Life

The Servant With One Talent:
Five Success Principles from the Greatest Parable Ever Told

The Cabin at the End of the Train:
A story about pursuing dreams

Acknowledgments

Editor:
Madeleine Eno has without doubt made me a better writer. I am grateful for her work on this book!

Illustrator:
Jesse Hostetler, thank you for your incredible illustrations!

Made in the USA
Middletown, DE
22 March 2023